Cognitive-Behavioral Coping
Skills Therapy Manual

National Institute on Alcohol Abuse and Alcoholism
Project MATCH Monograph Series
Volume 3

COGNITIVE-BEHAVIORAL COPING SKILLS THERAPY MANUAL

A Clinical Research Guide for Therapists Treating Individuals With Alcohol Abuse and Dependence

Compiled and edited by:

Ronald Kadden, Ph.D.
Kathleen Carroll, Ph.D.
Dennis Donovan, Ph.D.
Ned Cooney, Ph.D.
Peter Monti, Ph.D.
David Abrams, Ph.D.
Mark Litt, Ph.D.
Reid Hester, Ph.D.

Project MATCH Monograph Series Editor:
Margaret E. Mattson, Ph.D.

U.S. Department of Health and Human Services
Public Health Service
National Institutes of Health

National Institute on Alcohol Abuse and Alcoholism
6000 Executive Boulevard
Rockville, Maryland 20892–7003

Acknowledgments

Project MATCH Research Group and Other Contributors

Principal and Coinvestigators at the Sites

William Miller, Ph.D.
Reid Hester, Ph.D.
Center on Alcoholism, Substance Abuse and Addictions
University of New Mexico
Albuquerque, NM

Gerard Connors, Ph.D.
Robert Rychtarik, Ph.D.
Research Institute on Alcoholism
Buffalo, NY

Carrie Randall, Ph.D.
Raymond Anton, M.D.
Medical University of South Carolina and
    Veterans Administration Medical Center
Charleston, SC

Ronald Kadden, Ph.D.
Ned Cooney, Ph.D.
University of Connecticut School of Medicine
Farmington, CT

Carlo DiClemente, Ph.D.
Joseph Carbonari, Ed.D.
University of Houston
Houston, TX

Allen Zweben, DSW
University of Wisconsin-Milwaukee
Milwaukee, WI

Richard Longabaugh, Ed.D.
Robert Stout, Ph.D.
Brown University
Providence, RI

Dale Walker, M.D.
Dennis Donovan, Ph.D.
University of Washington and Seattle VA Medical Center
Seattle, WA

**Coordinating
Center
Principal and
Coinvestigators**

Thomas Babor, Ph.D.
Frances Del Boca, Ph.D.
University of Connecticut
Farmington, CT

Kathleen Carroll, Ph.D.
Bruce Rounsaville, M.D.
Yale University
New Haven, CT

**Contributing
Authors**

Peter Monti, Ph.D.
David Abrams, Ph.D.
Butler Hospital / Brown University
Providence, RI

Mark Litt, Ph.D.
University of Connecticut Health Center
Farmington, CT

NIAAA staff

John Allen, Ph.D.
Project Officer for Project MATCH
Chief, Treatment Research Branch

Margaret Mattson, Ph.D.
Staff Collaborator for Project MATCH

**Cooperative
Education
Program**

Lisa Marshall
Gallaudet University
Washington, DC

Consultants

Larry Muenz, Ph.D.
Gaithersburg, MD

Philip Wirtz, Ph.D.
George Washington University
Washington, DC

Contractor

Jane K. Myers
President
Janus Associates
Bethesda, MD

Foreword

A major focus of the efforts of the National Institute on Alcohol Abuse and Alcoholism (NIAAA) in treatment research is to rigorously test the patient-treatment matching approach to the clinical management of alcoholism. This commitment is particularly reflected in its multisite clinical trial, Project MATCH. This study is the first national, multisite trial of patient-treatment matching and one of the two largest current initiatives of NIAAA. Established under a cooperative agreement that allows direct collaboration between the Institute and the researcher, the project involves nine geographically representative clinical sites and a data coordinating center. Researchers in Project MATCH are among the most senior and experienced treatment scientists in the field. Both public and private treatment facilities, as well as hospital and university outpatient facilities, are represented.

The manuals in this series are the result of the collaborative efforts of the Project MATCH investigators and are used as guides by therapists in the trial. They are presented to the alcohol research community as standardized, well-documented intervention tools for alcoholism treatment research. The final reports of Project MATCH will inform us on the relative efficacy of the interventions being evaluated in the trial and on the types of clients who benefit the most from each of the therapies.

Until the final results from Project MATCH are presented to the community, these interim manuals will summarize the consensus of the investigators on reasonable intervention approaches based on present knowledge. We look forward to offering further refinements of these approaches as Project MATCH data are analyzed and published and as the alcohol treatment field advances through the efforts of other ongoing research.

Enoch Gordis, M.D.
Director
National Institute on Alcohol Abuse and
    Alcoholism

Preface

This manual for therapists is provided to the public to permit replication of the treatment procedures employed in Project MATCH, a multisite clinical trial of patient-treatment matching sponsored by the National Institute on Alcohol Abuse and Alcoholism (NIAAA). It describes Cognitive-Behavioral Coping Skills Therapy (CBT), one of three treatment approaches studied in Project MATCH. Therapist manuals for the other treatments—Twelve-Step Facilitation Therapy (TSF) and Motivational Enhancement Therapy (MET)—are available in volumes 1 and 2 of this series, respectively.

Rationale for Patient-Treatment Matching

Although a number of therapies have had varying degrees of success, no single treatment has been shown to be effective for all individuals diagnosed with alcohol abuse or dependence. In recent years, interest in the field has increasingly focused on patient-treatment matching to improve outcome. The hypothesis is that more beneficial results can be obtained if treatment is prescribed on the basis of individual patient needs and characteristics as opposed to treating all patients with the same diagnosis in the same manner.

Many investigators have turned their attention from main effects evaluations (i.e., studies that ask whether one intervention is more effective than another) to studies specifically designed to identify interactions between particular treatments and patient variables. While treatments may not appear to differ in effectiveness when applied to a heterogeneous client population, specific treatments may indeed be more or less effective for specific, clinically meaningful subgroups.

This reasoning has led to a new generation of alcoholism treatment research studies whose design is driven by the objective of finding effective "matches." Ultimately, the goal of this line of research is to provide the clinician with valid and practical rules applicable across a variety of treatment settings to assign patients to those treatment regimens particularly suited to them.

Project MATCH: An Overview

Project MATCH, a 5-year study, was initiated by the Treatment Research Branch of NIAAA in 1989. The details of the design and implementation of Project MATCH will be described in full in forthcoming publications. This section outlines the major features of the study.

The objective of Project MATCH is to determine if varying subgroups of alcohol abusing or dependent patients respond differentially to three treatments: (1) Twelve-Step Facilitation Therapy, (2) Cognitive-Behavioral Coping Skills Therapy, and (3) Motivational Enhancement Therapy. Each treatment is delivered during a 12-week period by trained therapists following a standardized protocol.

The project consists of two independent treatment-matching studies, one with clients recruited at five outpatient settings, the second with patients receiving aftercare treatment at four sites following an episode of standard inpatient treatment. Patients are randomly assigned to one of the three treatment approaches. Each study evaluates the interaction effects between selected patient characteristics and the three treatments.

Each of the nine study sites is recruiting approximately 150–200 clients. Clients are evaluated at intake and again at 3, 6, 9, 12, and 15 months. Outcome measures for the trial include drinking behavior, psychological and social function, and consequences of drinking. Analyses of a priori hypotheses, as well as exploratory analyses, will show whether different patient characteristics are associated with differential treatment outcomes in each of the three therapeutic interventions.

Cognitive-Behavioral Therapy. This therapy is based on the principles of social learning theory and views drinking behavior as functionally related to major problems in the person's life. It posits that addressing this broad spectrum of problems will prove more effective than focusing on drinking alone. Emphasis is placed on overcoming skill deficits and increasing the person's ability to cope with high-risk situations that commonly precipitate relapse, including both interpersonal difficulties and intrapersonal discomfort, such as anger or depression. The program consists of 12 sessions with the goal of training the individual to use active behavioral or cognitive coping methods to deal with problems, rather than relying on alcohol as a maladaptive coping strategy. The skills also provide a means of obtaining social support critical to the maintenance of sobriety.

Twelve-Step Facilitation Approach. This therapy is grounded in the concept of alcoholism as a spiritual and medical disease. The content of this intervention is consistent with the 12 Steps of Alcoholics Anonymous (AA), with primary emphasis given to Steps 1 though 5. In addition to abstinence from alcohol, a major goal of the treatment is to foster the patient's commitment to participation in AA. During the course of the program's 12 sessions, patients are actively encouraged to attend AA meetings and to maintain journals of their AA attendance and participation. Therapy sessions are highly structured, following a similar format each week that includes symptoms inquiry, review and reinforcement for AA participation, introduction and explication of the week's theme, and setting goals for AA participation for the next week. Material introduced during treatment sessions is complemented by reading assignments from AA literature.

Motivational Enhancement Therapy. MET is based on principles of motivational psychology and is designed to produce rapid, internally motivated change. This treatment strategy does not attempt to guide and train the client, step by step, through recovery, but instead employs motivational strategies to mobilize the client's own resources. MET consists of four carefully planned and individualized treatment sessions. The first two sessions focus on structured feedback from the initial assessment, future plans, and motivation for change. The final two sessions at the midpoint and end of treatment provide opportunities for the therapist to reinforce progress, encourage reassessment, and provide an objective perspective on the process of change.

Caveats and Critical Considerations

Although all three manuals were developed for a randomized clinical trial focusing on patient-treatment matching hypotheses, the substance of the interventions is equally suitable for other research questions and designs. However, the reader needs to be aware of the parameters of Project MATCH.

Therapy is delivered in a structured research situation. All three treatments are manual guided and administered by experienced therapists who receive specialized training in one of the three project interventions. Therapists closely follow the procedures outlined in their manual, with regular supervision (by observation of videotapes) from both local and projectwide clinical supervisors.

This manual is written for therapists with similar intensive training and supervision. A summary of the procedures used to select, train, and supervise therapists in Project MATCH is provided in appendix B.

There is an important difference between a therapy textbook and a therapy manual. A therapy *textbook* is a comprehensive presentation of a particular therapeutic approach, usually describing a conceptual model, general principles, and a broad range of applications and examples. It is typically meant to facilitate broad utilization of a therapeutic approach by a wide range of practitioners in a variety of settings. A therapy *manual*, on the other hand, is intended to operationalize and standardize a treatment approach to be used in a particular context, usually a specific clinical trial. In writing a therapy manual, the authors must make a number of specific decisions (e.g., the number and timing of sessions, the content of each session) that are ordinarily left to clinical judgment in a therapy textbook.

This manual is designed to standardize CBT as a 12-session treatment modality within the particular context of Project MATCH. All treatments are preceded by the same extensive assessment battery, requiring approximately 7–8 hours. Abstinence is the expressed goal of all treatments, and except in unusual situations, all sessions are videotaped. Each treatment session is preceded by a breath test to ensure sobriety, and a positive breath alcohol reading results in rescheduling the session. Therapists are prohibited from mixing CBT with other treatment approaches, and the purity of approach is maintained by local and national supervisors who review videotapes. All therapy has to be completed within 90 days. A significant other can be invited to participate in up to two sessions.

Other design requirements of clinical trials are likewise standardized across all sites, including features such as defined patient eligibility criteria, randomized assignment of treatment, and guidelines for dealing with patients who are late or absent for treatment sessions or who show significant clinical deterioration during the course of the intervention. Guidelines regulate and document the amount and type of therapy over and above that provided by Project MATCH that a client receives during the study. Data collection and delivery of treatment are kept strictly separate, with the former being handled by research assistants under the supervision of the project coordinators. The three manuals refer to these Project MATCH-specific procedures with the knowledge that some readers may wish to follow similar guidelines, while others may choose to devise new guidelines more appropriate to the requirements of their own project.

The therapeutic approach that underlies this manual is described in the references cited in the bibliography. The specific session-by-session instructions to the therapists were drawn from a number of sources. Chief among these was a previously published therapists' manual, *Treating Alcohol Dependence: A Coping Skills Training Guide* by Monti, Abrams, Kadden, and Cooney (1989). The integration of material from the Monti text and other source material as well as the modifications introduced to address the requirements of Project MATCH are described in detail in the introduction.

The general therapeutic principles underlying CBT can be applied in many other ways than those delineated here. Under ordinary circumstances, the number, duration, and distribution of sessions could be flexible. Significant others might be involved in all sessions or none at all. The goals of therapy might be more flexible, and cognitive-behavioral procedures could be intermixed with other therapeutic strategies. The specific prescriptions outlined in this manual are imposed for purposes of standardization and separation of treatments in Project MATCH.

The staff of Project MATCH and NIAAA make no claims or guarantees regarding the effectiveness of the treatment procedures described in this manual. Although the principles of CBT are well-grounded in clinical and experimental research, the specific efficacy of CBT as outlined in this manual remains to be tested. The final reports of Project MATCH will provide clearer information on the efficacy of this approach relative to others and on the types of clients for whom it may be optimal. In the interim, this manual offers a detailed description of CBT procedures as constructed by consensus among the investigators and implemented by the therapists of Project MATCH. All manuals of this kind should be regarded as under development and subject to ongoing improvement based on subsequent research and experience.

The planning and operation of Project MATCH and the products now resulting from it, including this series of manuals, reflect the efforts of many individuals over a period of several years. Their dedication and collegial collaboration have been remarkable and will enrich the field of alcoholism treatment research for years to come.

> Margaret E. Mattson, Ph.D.
> Project MATCH Staff Collaborator
> Project MATCH Monograph Series Editor
> Division of Clinical and Prevention
>   Research
> National Institute on Alcohol Abuse and
>   Alcoholism

Contents

Introduction

The interventions to be tested in Project MATCH were selected by the trial's Steering Committee, a group composed of the principal investigators of the participating sites and a representative of the National Institute on Alcohol Abuse and Alcoholism (NIAAA). It was agreed that a cognitive-behavior therapy (CBT) approach would be among the treatments offered and that a recently published book, *Treating Alcohol Dependence: A Coping Skills Training Guide* by Monti, Abrams, Kadden, and Cooney (1989), would be the basic manual for this approach. This manual had been used in several treatment matching studies (Kadden et al. 1989; Monti et al. 1990; Rohsenow et al. 1991; Cooney et al. 1991) and seemed generally well suited for the requirements of Project MATCH.

This manual contains material for 22 sessions—8 core or required sessions that are implemented with all subjects and 14 elective sessions, of which 4 are selected for each subject. Thus, each subject receives a total of 12 sessions composed of a fixed set of core sessions and several elective sessions chosen for the individual patient.

Sixteen sessions are taken from the Monti et al. text. Rather than reproduce entire sessions from Monti et al. here, the present manual makes extensive reference to treatment sessions in the Monti et al. book and describes departures from them. Thus, this publication is not the exact document that the Project MATCH CBT therapists worked from, but it contains sufficient material and references so that anyone could replicate the protocol employed in Project MATCH by using this manual and the Monti et al. book conjointly.

The six sessions that were not drawn from Monti et al. are reprinted in full. Numerous other sources (see appendix A) contributed to these sessions, and they are gratefully acknowledged.

Given the extensive overlap between this manual and Monti et al., it is reasonable to ask why this version merits separate publication. There have been numerous requests for the Project MATCH treatment manuals for use in other research studies. It was felt that the exact protocols that were employed should be furnished to the community at large for those desiring to replicate the Project MATCH treatments.

This accounts for the format of the present volume, with new material being printed in full but without reprinting published material that is generally available. The only exception to this is the introductory chapter where, for reasons of comprehensibility, all of the text is presented, including the material taken directly from Monti et al.

Modifications to Monti et al.

The modifications made to the basic Monti et al. book to accommodate Project MATCH and the decisionmaking processes that led to them are summarized below.

Additions

The Project MATCH Steering Committee decided to include some additional elements of the Community Reinforcement Approach (Sisson and Azrin 1989) because of its demonstrated success in several clinical trials. The added elements were marital counseling, training in job seeking and interviewing skills, and expanded material on coping with cravings and urges to drink. Another session focusing specifically on negative moods was added to the four on negative thinking and anger already present, because depression is a widespread problem among recovering alcoholics.

Group Versus Individual Therapy

The Monti et al. book is built around a group therapy approach to treatment, although it does contain a section discussing adaptation to the individual treatment setting. The Steering Committee considered the advantages and disadvantages of both group and individual approaches for the Project MATCH trial.

The advantages of group therapy include its widespread use in alcoholism rehabilitation; the potential facilitative effect of a group's social environment on cognitive, affective, and behavioral changes; the support system that groups provide for newly recovering clients; and the potential for cost savings with group compared to individual treatment. However, group therapy presented a number of problems from the research perspective. Clients might have to wait weeks before beginning treatment while groups were being assembled; it is more difficult to assess the therapist factor in outcome, and some argue that the groups (as opposed to individual clients) should be considered as the unit of analysis (e.g., Kaul and Bednar 1986). To properly evaluate the treatment, an individual therapy format was selected. This meant that some of the wording in Monti et al. had to be edited to reflect the dyadic therapeutic relationship, and some of the group-oriented role playing exercises had to be restructured. In the present manual, minor modifications of role-plays are described in terms of the changes made to the Monti et al. book. When the changes were substantial, the modified exercises are presented verbatim.

Whenever reference is made to material in the Monti et al. book, it is left to the reader to insert needed transpositions in the text from group to individual therapy.

Length of Treatment

The Monti et al. book presents 27 treatment sessions. With increasing pressures on clinicians to reduce the length of treatment, a clinical trial involving a 6-month treatment protocol would have been excessively long. The Project MATCH Steering Committee decided upon a 12-week duration for each study treatment. To best use the breadth of material in Monti et al. to meet clients' needs, while at the same time assuring that all clients received certain essential sessions, the choice was made to have eight core sessions (introductory, termination, and six additional sessions) and to allow the therapist and client to jointly select the four most appropriate from among 14 elective sessions.

Supporting Data

The final chapter in Monti et al. describes empirical findings that have been obtained using its treatment materials. What follows is a summary of studies using the Monti et al. book that have appeared since its publication.

The treatment sessions in the Monti et al. book were designed to address both interpersonal and intrapersonal coping skills. The final chapter described a treatment study in which these two types of sessions were compared: alcoholics were randomly assigned to a "standard treatment" combined with (1) cognitive-behavioral mood management, (2) individual communication skills training, or (3) communication training with a significant other present. Recently published results indicate that while all treatment groups improved significantly in a role-play assessment of coping skills and showed reduced anxiety in both general and alcohol-specific role-play situations (Monti et al. 1990), patients who received either of the communications skills training packages improved the most in the alcohol-specific role-play assessment. Followup results at 6 months after treatment showed that alcoholics who received communication skills training, with or without family involvement, consumed significantly less alcohol than alcoholics who received cognitive-behavioral mood management training. Rohsenow et al. (1991) found that individual or family communication skills training benefited a broader spectrum of patients, regardless of initial level of education, alcohol dependence, skill, anxiety, or beliefs, when compared to mood management training.

The Monti et al. book described another patient-treatment matching study by Kadden et al. (1989) in which inpatients were randomly assigned to aftercare consisting of either interactional group therapy or CBT groups using Monti et al. as the treatment manual. Survival analyses provided evidence for the durability of matching interactions over a 2-year outcome assessment period (Cooney et al. 1991). Relapse occurred more slowly when clients having more psychopathology or sociopathy received CBT rather than interactional therapy. For those clients evidencing little psychopathology or sociopathy, relapse occurred more slowly when they received interactional therapy rather than CBT. Clients who were "matched" according to these results had 2-year abstinence rates of about 45 percent, whereas those who were mismatched sustained only a 25-percent abstinent rate. Clients classified as cognitively impaired had better outcomes in interactional therapy and worse outcomes in the CBT groups.

In other analyses on the same data set, trained raters analyzed audiotape recordings of treatment sessions to assess the discriminability of the two treatments (Getter et al. 1992). They found that CBT sessions were characterized by significantly more educational and skill-training activities, application of problem-solving techniques, role playing, and identification of high-risk situations. Interactional sessions produced significantly more expression of feelings, interpersonal learning, and here-and-now focus.

Another analysis was based on two clusters of variables that characterized the clients at intake to the study (Litt et al. 1992). Clients in the less severe cluster fared better in interactional treatment, whereas those classified in the more severe cluster had better outcomes in CBT.

Role-play assessments (Abrams et al. 1991; Monti et al. 1990, 1992) were used to examine the relationship between clients' coping skills and the two treatments offered. CBT resulted in better treatment outcomes for those with poorer observer-rated coping skills, greater observer-rated anxiety, or greater self-reported urge to drink in the role-play assessments. Interactional therapy was better for those with greater skill, less anxiety, or fewer urges to drink in the role plays (Kadden et al. in press).

These findings indicate the usefulness of this version of CBT for clinical research studies of patient-treatment matching and begin to delineate some of the parameters that define the clients for whom it will be the most appropriate treatment.

> Ronald Kadden
> Ned Cooney
> Peter Monti
> David Abrams
> Authors of *Treating Alcohol Dependence: A Coping Skills Training Guide*

References

Abrams, D.B.; Binkoff, J.A.; Zwick, W.R.; Liepman, M.R.; Nirenberg, T.D.; Munroe, S.M.; and Monti, P.M. Alcohol abusers' and social drinkers' responses to alcohol-relevant and general situations. *Journal of Studies on Alcohol* 52:409–414, 1991.

Cooney, N.L.; Kadden, R.M.; Litt, M.D.; and Getter, H. Matching alcoholics to coping skills or interactional therapies: Two-year followup results. *Journal of Consulting and Clinical Psychology* 59:598–601, 1991.

Getter, H.; Litt, M.D.; Kadden, R.M.; and Cooney, N.L. Measuring treatment process in coping skills and interactional group therapies for alcoholism. *International Journal of Group Psychotherapy* 42:419–430, 1992.

Kadden, R.M.; Cooney, N.L.; Getter, H.; and Litt, M.D. Matching alcoholics to coping skills or interactional therapies: Posttreatment results. *Journal of Consulting and Clinical Psychology* 57:698–704, 1989.

Kadden, R.M.; Litt, M.D.; Cooney, N.L.; and Busher, D.A. Relationship between role-play measures of coping skills and alcoholism treatment outcome. *Addictive Behaviors*, in press.

Kaul, T.J., and Bednar, R.L. Experiential group research: Results, questions and suggestions. In: Garfield, S.L., and Bergin, A.E., eds. *Handbook of Psychotherapy and Behavior Change*. 3rd edition. New York: Wiley, 1986. pp. 671–714.

Litt, M.D.; Babor, T.F.; DelBoca, F.K.; Kadden, R.M.; and Cooney, N.L. Types of alcoholics: II. Application of an empirically-derived typology to treatment matching. *Archives of General Psychiatry* 49:609–614, 1992.

Monti, P.M.; Abrams, D.B.; Binkoff, J.A.; Zwick, W.R.; Liepman, M.R.; Nirenberg, T.D.; and Rohsenow, D.J. Communication skills training, communication skills training with family and cognitive-behavioral mood management training for alcoholics. *Journal of Studies on Alcohol* 51:263–270, 1990.

Monti, P.M.; Abrams, D.B.; Kadden, R.M.; and Cooney, N.L. *Treating Alcohol Dependence: A Coping Skills Training Guide*. New York: Guilford, 1989.

Monti, P.M.; Rohsenow, D.R.; Abrams, D.B.; Zwick, W.R.; Binkoff, J.A.; Munroe, S.M.; Fingeret, A.L.; Nirenberg, T.D.; Liepman, M.R.; Pedraza, M.; Kadden, R.M.; and Cooney, N.L. Development of a behavior analytically derived alcohol specific role play assessment instrument. Manuscript in submission, 1992.

Rohsenow, D.R.; Monti, P.M.; Binkoff, J.A.; Liepman, M.R.; Nirenberg, T.D.; and Abrams, D.B. Patient-treatment matching for alcoholic men in communication skills versus cognitive-behavioral mood management training. *Addictive Behaviors* 16:63–69, 1991.

Sisson, R.W., and Azrin, N.H. The community reinforcement approach. In: Hester, R.K., and Miller, W.R., eds. *Handbook of Alcoholism Treatment Approaches: Effective Alternatives*. New York: Pergamon, 1989.

Overview of the Program

The treatment approach specified in this manual is based upon a cognitive-behavioral model, with a focus on the training of interpersonal and self-management skills. Research has provided some evidence for the efficacy of cognitive-behavioral approaches with alcoholic patients, but considerably more detailed information is needed. The present manual provides a basis for advancing that work by presenting a clearly specified treatment that can be reliably delivered, monitored, and evaluated.

Rationale for Outpatient Treatment

Outpatient treatment offers considerable opportunity for interaction between the treatment program and the realities of each client's daily existence. The events of clients' daily lives can be described in treatment sessions and used as the basis for problem-solving exercises, role plays, and homework assignments. Outpatients have the advantage of being able to practice new skills in a variety of problem situations. This greatly enhances generalization of new behaviors to various aspects of a client's natural environment. In addition, the outpatient therapist can provide session-by-session monitoring of progress in applying new skills and supervised problem solving to deal with difficulties as they arise.

Treatment Goals

The primary goal of this treatment is to master skills that will help to maintain abstinence from alcohol and other drugs. In order to develop these skills, clients must identify high-risk situations that may increase the likelihood of renewed drinking. These high-risk situations include precipitants of drinking that are external to the individual as well as internal events such as cognitions and emotions.

Having identified situations that represent a high risk for relapse to drinking, clients must develop skills to cope with them. In this program, all clients are first taught basic skill elements for dealing with common high-risk problem areas; they are encouraged to engage in

NOTE: This overview makes extensive use of material from chapter 4, "Treatment Considerations for Inpatient and Outpatient Settings" (Monti et al. 1989). © Guilford Press. Used with permission.

problem solving, role playing, and homework practice exercises that will enable participants to apply the new skills to meet their own particular needs.

Client Role

Cognitive behavioral treatment for alcohol abuse requires active participation by individual clients as well as their assumption of responsibility for learning the necessary self-control skills to prevent future abuse. Through active participation in a training program in which new skills and cognitive strategies are acquired, an individual's maladaptive habits can be replaced with healthy behaviors regulated by cognitive processes involving awareness and responsible planning.

Patients must get a chance to build their actual skills during role plays and to receive constructive feedback using relevant (client-centered) problems rather than simply discussing or reflecting on material. Active participation, modeling, and practice with positive, corrective feedback are the most effective ways to modify self-efficacy expectations and create long-lasting behavior change.

Therapist Role

Since behavioral approaches to treatment are sometimes misunderstood as "cookbooks" to be applied without careful consideration of the unique needs of the individual receiving treatment, it is important that therapists be experienced in psychotherapy skills as well as behavioral principles. In addition, they must have good interpersonal skills and be familiar with the materials so as to impart skills successfully and serve as credible models. They must be willing to play a very active role in this type of directive therapy.

Despite this behavioral approach, many of the basic rules for conducting psychotherapy apply. Therapists must use many traditional therapy skills (e.g., establishing rapport, limit setting, empathy), while functioning as active teachers and role models.

Prior to each treatment session, therapists are encouraged to reread relevant sections of the manual. To ensure that the main points of each session are covered, we recommend outlining them or highlighting them in the text. In presenting the didactic material, we suggest briefly paraphrasing the main points and listing them on a chalkboard or flipchart.

Although standardization is essential when conducting a clinical trial, and covering all important points is desirable, it is essential that the desire to comply with the treatment protocol not lead to reading to clients from the text. As long as the major points are covered, a natural, free-flowing presentation style is preferred. It is crucial that clients not get the message that the therapist's agenda of adhering strictly to the manual is more important than the issues and concerns that constitute the client's personal agenda.

Indeed, if clients are not routinely involved and encouraged to provide their own material as examples, we have found that treatment becomes boring and the energy level for learning drops off dramatically. Therapists may experience burnout as a result. Effective reinforcement of clients for their active participation can help prevent burnout on the part of both clients and therapists.

The "Rationale" and "Skill Guidelines" sections of each session are intended to provide therapists with adequate background information to guide discussion of the topic. Although the topics covered usually generate discussion that is meaningful, the discussion must be shaped by the therapist to prevent it from shifting focus onto other clinical issues. Since the treatment session can pass very quickly, it is important that the therapist keep the presentation of the rationale and skill guidelines brief, to allow adequate time for role playing, feedback, and discussion.

One self-disclosure issue likely to come up at the beginning of therapy is the drinking practice of the therapist.[1] Therapists differ as to whether or not to answer this question directly; however, we agree with Vannicelli that the real concern that is usually being expressed is "Will you, therapist, be able to understand me, and can I get the kind of help here that I need?" (p. 21). Thus, although we leave the specific answer to this question up to the therapists' judgment and individual therapeutic styles, we do encourage them to acknowledge to the client asking the question that they hear the underlying message. Acknowledgment of the clients' underlying concern, coupled with an invitation to clients to judge the value of this program for themselves, usually is adequate.

Adherence to the Manual

When using this manual in a controlled research project, it is crucial that the guidelines in the manual be strictly followed. Deviations will add "noise" to the study, and supervision will therefore focus on adherence to the manual. If the concept of manual-based treatment is troublesome, or if any of the demands made by this particular manual seem difficult to follow or are incompatible with a therapist's style or beliefs, this should be discussed in supervision as soon as possible.

Menu of Topics

A word is needed about the sequence in which clients are exposed to the various topics. An ambulatory program presents an inherent conflict regarding the order in which skills are taught and rehearsed.

---

1 Vannicelli, M. Group therapy with alcoholics: Special techniques. *Journal of Studies on Alcohol* 43:17–37, 1982.

Good teaching practice demands that skills be taught in a logical sequence, in which more basic topics are covered first and serve as the foundation for subsequent presentation of higher order skills. However, there is a conflicting need to help clients deal with immediate threats to their sobriety, which may lead them to an early relapse and undermine their continuation in the program. Therefore, sessions such as "Managing Thoughts About Alcohol" and "Drink Refusal Skills," which might otherwise have come late in the program after more fundamental skills have been acquired, are instead presented early to give clients the tools to cope with situations that may overwhelm them and lead them to relapse or drop out of treatment. Another session, "Problem Solving," consists of a complex set of cognitive skills that would be more appropriately taught late in the program but is instead also presented early to provide clients and therapists with a common language and framework for dealing with problems and crises in clients' lives that can lead to early relapse. Following these sessions, other topics may be selected based on their potential for helping clients cope with high-risk situations that they may face or based on the client's apparent skills deficits.

This cognitive-behavioral treatment program is composed of eight core elements to which all the clients will be exposed. There is also a menu of additional sessions that may be selected based on the therapist's assessment of a client's problems or on needs or desires expressed by the client. Although it may be obvious to the therapist which of the elective topics should be included, it is advised that clients be allowed to participate as much as possible in making the selection. If a difference of opinion on the choice of sessions arises between clients and therapist, it is probably advisable to defer to the patients, in the interest of maximizing their involvement in treatment.

Outpatient Versus Aftercare Settings

The overall treatment goals and methods are the same for those sites doing outpatient or aftercare treatment. At the outpatient treatment sites, however, the focus is more on achieving abstinence and managing some of the problems of early recovery. The choice among which optional sessions to include may be determined in part by problems that are likely to pose an imminent threat to the client's sobriety.

At the aftercare sites, the focus is more on maintenance of sobriety. Clients have already been exposed to an intensive treatment program and may have received training in some of the skills offered here. They nevertheless should be given all the core elements of this program, but the choice among the optional sessions may be guided by a client's need for additional skill building or by topics that may not have been covered during the prior treatment.

Discussion of Clients' Recent Problems

Clients experience numerous problems, cravings, and actual slips as they struggle with sobriety. Although the focus of the sessions must be on the structured program, ignoring clients' real life problems entails the risk that they will view treatment as peripheral or irrelevant to their current needs. As a compromise between the demands of the protocol and the clients' perceived needs, it is suggested that 15–20 minutes be spent at the outset of each session discussing current problems.

Efforts should be made to structure these discussions along lines that are consistent with a skills-training approach. This can be accomplished most easily using the problem-solving format presented in session 3. In subsequent sessions, this format should be used whenever possible in discussing clients' problems. However, problem solving will not be appropriate for all situations that are brought up. In such instances, a functional analysis may be helpful, focusing on identification of the ABC's (antecedents, behavior, consequences) and on ways that the patient can try to change them. The general rule is that these opening discussions should be structured along behavioral lines to keep them consistent with the approach of this manual.

There is frequently conflict between the desire of clients to get help with their immediate problems and the desire of the therapist to get on with the day's agenda. As a result, the first phase of a session often lasts longer than the therapist would like but shorter than the client desires. Clients must be reminded that this time-limited therapy cannot always explore problems to the point of complete resolution. In Project MATCH, if serious problems arise repeatedly, the project coordinator is consulted. Criteria have been developed to determine if additional treatment is needed or if participation in the program is in the patient's best interest.

Structure of Sessions

After the initial period of supportive therapy, the structured portion of the session is initiated with a review of the skills taught in the preceding session and of the homework assignment. New material is then introduced, beginning with the rationale, which emphasizes the relationship of the new skills both to maintaining sobriety and to dealing with problems that are commonly faced by recovering alcoholics. The skill guidelines are presented verbally, listed on a chalkboard or poster board, and printed in handouts for the client to take home. It is critically important that therapists not spend large amounts of time lecturing to clients. It is essential that the therapist solicit input and reactions from the clients during the presentation of the rationale and skill guidelines sections to engage their interest and prevent them from tuning out. Therapists model the performance of the skills, and clients are then encouraged to generate role-play scenes based on their daily experience.

Role playing is viewed as a critical part of the experience, and at least one-third of each session should be allocated to it. Nevertheless, it is sometimes a struggle to engage clients in role plays. Therapists may have to provide considerable structure and encouragement to get the process underway.

There is a danger that, with such a full agenda and such highly structured sessions, the clients may come to feel that the therapist's agenda is more important than their own needs. Therefore, it is essential that the therapist not read from written material or be too rigid in following the set agenda and strive as much as possible to provide examples from material that the client has previously brought up. Usually this is not difficult, because the skills-training sessions cover commonly encountered problems that are likely to have been raised already by the client. Occasionally, it is necessary to sharply curtail a session's agenda in order to deal with some individual crisis. However, this should be a rare event and avoided as much as possible.

Guidelines for Behavior Rehearsal Role Plays

Behavior rehearsal plays a central part in this skills-training program and is the main strategy by which clients acquire new skills. Each session provides a safe haven where clients can practice and improve their skills prior to trying them in the real world. Although some amount of discussion during the introduction to each new skill is useful, therapists should discourage lengthy discussion about problem situations and instead should focus on setting up and processing role plays.

Clients normally feel a bit uncomfortable or embarrassed at first about role playing. Therapists should acknowledge that this is a normal reaction and that behavior rehearsal becomes easier after a few experiences with it. After a while, participants are able to get into a scene more realistically and to focus on their role in it. Resistance can take subtle forms, such as focusing on other issues or asking many questions. Therapists can acknowledge that they also feel uncomfortable role playing. They may have to take the lead and demonstrate the first role plays.

Therapists should encourage clients initially to generate and describe personally relevant scenes that are of only moderate difficulty. As clients demonstrate ability to handle these situations effectively, they should be encouraged to generate and practice more difficult ones. An adequate description of a scene will include specifying where it takes place, what the primary problems are, whom the role play partner should portray (boss, stranger, child, spouse, date), relevant behaviors of the person portrayed so that the partner can act accordingly, and specification of the client's goal in the interaction.

The following strategies are useful in helping clients to generate scenes:

- Ask clients to recall a situation in the recent past where use of the new skill being taught would have been desirable (e.g., a client wanted to start a conversation but could not; another yelled at a neighbor about an unleashed dog tearing up the garden; another wanted to express positive feelings toward his spouse but could not without drinking first).

- Ask clients to anticipate a difficult situation that may arise in the near future and that calls for use of the skill (e.g., a client's apartment has been cold this winter and she wants to ask the building owner to raise the setting on the thermostat; another client is going to a retirement party this weekend and will be offered alcoholic drinks).

- Therapists can suggest appropriate situations based on their knowledge of a client's recent circumstances.

It is essential that every role play be effectively processed. It is an opportunity for clients to receive praise/recognition for practice and improvement as well as constructive criticism about the less effective elements of their behavior. During this portion of the session, the therapist's primary goals are to identify specific problem areas and to shape and reinforce successive approximations to more effective communication skills.

Immediately after every role play, the therapist should reinforce the client for participating. Next, the therapist and the client should both give their reactions to the performance (e.g., How does the protagonist feel about the way he handled the situation? What effect did the interaction have on the partner?).

The therapist then offers comments about the role play. These comments should be both supportive/reinforcing and constructively critical. If a role play performance has several deficiencies, the therapist should choose only one or two to work on at a time. All positive and negative feedback should focus on specific aspects of the person's behavior, since global evaluations do not pinpoint what was particularly effective or ineffective. Finally, the praise/reinforcement provided should always be sincere. The therapist should refrain from being unnecessarily effusive so that the value of the positive feedback is not undermined. Therapists may repeat a scene to give clients an opportunity to try out the feedback they received the first time around.

"Role reversal" is a role-play strategy in which the therapist models use of a new skill, with the client playing the role of the target person (e.g., spouse, employer, neighbor). This strategy is particularly useful if clients are having difficulty using a skill or are pessimistic about the effectiveness of a suggested communication approach. By playing the "other," they have an opportunity to observe and to experience first-hand the effects of the suggested skill.

Homework

Homework is a powerful adjunct to treatment, because real life situations can be utilized for practice, enhancing the likelihood that these behaviors will be repeated in similar situations (generalization). A preplanned homework exercise has been designed for every session of this program. Most require that the clients try in a real life situation what they have already role played in the session. The homework assignment also requires that the clients record facts concerning the setting, their behavior, the response they evoked, and an evaluation of the adequacy of their performance. Homework exercises can be modified to fit the specific details of individual situations more closely, and extra homework assignments are sometimes given to help clients cope with problem situations they have encountered.

Compliance with homework is often a problem in behavior therapy. A number of steps are taken to foster compliance:

- The assignments may be referred to as "practice exercises" to avoid the negative connotations often associated with the term "homework."

- When giving each assignment, the therapist should provide a careful rationale and description of the assignment.

- Ask the client what problems can be foreseen in completing the assignment, and discuss ways to overcome these obstacles.

- Ask clients to identify a specific time that can be set aside to work on the assignment.

- The therapist should review the preceding session's exercises at the beginning of each session, making an effort to praise all approximations to compliance with the assignment.

Although problems that clients have with the exercises should certainly be discussed and understood, the main emphasis is on reinforcing the positive aspects of performance. For those who did not do an assignment, discuss what could be done to ensure compliance with the next assignment. No contingencies other than social praise or disapproval are imposed by the therapists to enhance compliance with homework assignments.

Coping Skills Training With Significant Others

Clients are strongly urged to bring in their spouse, someone they live with, or a close supportive friend for two of the sessions. The emphasis in these sessions should be placed on interpersonal skills-training topics, saving the more individually focused cognitive and intrapersonal exercises for individual therapy sessions. Communication skills training can be beneficial to clients and significant others for reducing dysfunctional interactions.

As an illustration, a spouse may challenge/criticize an alcoholic in a suspicious manner that, while intended to prevent drinking, may actually exacerbate the situation and increase the likelihood of drinking. The client and spouse can be taught directly, in role plays with each other, how to give and receive criticism in a more adaptive fashion. If the role play and feedback reduce misunderstanding and improve communication, then maintenance of sobriety is more likely.

Occasionally, the relationship between a significant other and the alcoholic is so conflicted that effective role playing cannot take place. In these circumstances, it is helpful to first have the therapist model the skills in question. Following this, the significant other is paired with the therapist and the scenario is repeated. Next, the alcoholic role plays with the therapist. Finally, the alcoholic is paired with the significant other. By this time, after receiving feedback on several role plays, the pair may be better equipped to engage in effective role playing together.

In couples with a great deal of marital distress, it is best not to try to deal with all of the complex marital, and perhaps sexual dysfunction, issues. Limit the skills-training focus to more basic, safe skills (e.g., giving and receiving compliments, criticism, assertiveness, nonverbal behavior).

Although it is essential to explore communication concerning drinking behaviors and triggers of drinking, such exploration may lead to more deep-seated marital conflicts over trust, anger, intimacy, abandonment, dependency, and narcissistic needs. Sometimes these issues can be dealt with briefly, but they tend to require large amounts of time, and consequently the didactic skills materials may not get covered. The therapist needs to bring the focus back to the specific observable behaviors that appear to be functionally related to drinking or poor communication skills.

Preventing Attrition

In the first session, it is important to anticipate potential obstacles to successful treatment, especially factors that may lead to early attrition. Therefore, the therapist should explore any instances in which clients previously dropped out of treatment and advise clients that they should discuss any thoughts of quitting treatment. Such thoughts are not uncommon, and open discussion can resolve problems before clients drop out. Progress in treatment is not steady—there are ups and downs. Most clients experience hopelessness, anger, frustration, and other negative feelings at times. Clients should be advised to discuss such feelings, even if they fear that it might be embarrassing to the therapist.

It is useful for the therapist to point out that terminating treatment may be one of a series of "seemingly irrelevant decisions" that eventually lead to a client's later drinking. For this reason, any hint that a client is considering dropping out should be taken very seriously and fully discussed.

Many clients quit treatment after their first drinking episode. Clients should be warned that, even with efforts to maintain abstinence, some of them may slip and begin drinking. At the first session, they should be told not to come to treatment intoxicated, but they should be strongly encouraged to continue to attend after a drinking episode so that they can receive help in regaining sobriety, coping with their reaction to the slip, and avoiding future lapses.

There is a delicate balance between setting the stage for clients' feeling that it is permissible to return after a lapse and actually giving them permission to drink. Therapists should take care that clients understand this distinction.

Alcohol and Other Drug Use

Clients are asked to accept the goal of total abstinence from alcohol and all nonprescribed psychoactive drugs, at least for the duration of treatment. They are also asked to talk about any drinking or drug use that occurs and about any cravings or fears of relapse that they experience. They are told that it is common to have some ambivalent feelings about accepting abstinence as a goal, and they are encouraged to discuss these feelings as well as any actual slips that might occur. Clients are allowed to continue even after an episode of alcohol or other drug use, as long as they make the commitment to work toward renewed abstinence. However, they are asked not to come to a session under the influence of alcohol and other drugs because they would not be able to concentrate on or recall the topics covered.

In this program, anyone found to be under the influence of alcohol or other drugs is asked to leave the session. This is done in such a way that clients do not view it as a punishment; anyone asked to leave is encouraged to return to the next session sober and to continue in treatment.

Clients asked to leave are not allowed to drive themselves home. Their car keys are taken away, and they are asked to arrange safe transportation with a family member, a friend, or public transportation.

When discussing episodes of drinking or drug use, emphasize that these are common occurrences. An atmosphere of openness about this topic should be fostered. Clients are encouraged to conduct a functional analysis of their alcohol use and of urges to drink, identifying specific people, places, events, thoughts, emotions, and behaviors that preceded and followed the drinking or urges.

Clients are given specific guidelines for dealing with the immediate aftermath of a drinking episode. They are advised to get rid of the alcohol, remove themselves from the setting in which the drinking occurred, and call someone for help (a friend or spouse). They are cautioned about feelings of guilt and self-blame that often accompany a slip and are warned not to allow such reactions to prompt further drinking.

Guidelines are also given for dealing with the longer term impact of drinking episodes. Clients are urged to examine a slip with someone, not to sweep it under the rug. They are advised to analyze possible triggers, including the who, when, and where of the situation and anticipatory thoughts. Did they expect substance use to change something or meet some need? Reactions to the drinking episode should also be analyzed, including behavior, thoughts, and feelings, with special attention to feelings of guilt, depression, and self-blame. Clients are warned about catastrophizing thoughts, such as "Here I go again; I guess I'll never change" or "I'll quit again after I finish this bottle." If allowed to proceed unchecked, these common reactions can contribute to further drinking. The value of reminder cards, listing the troubles that addictive behavior has caused and the benefits that sobriety has brought, is stressed.

Absences

If a client does not come for a scheduled therapy session, the therapist should immediately attempt to contact the client by telephone to ascertain why the session was missed and to reschedule if possible. If the therapist is unable to contact the client within 2 days by telephone, a brief letter should be sent to the client. (In Project MATCH, the project coordinator is in charge of sending the letter). It is important that all reasonable efforts be made to keep clients in treatment. These efforts are continued until clients miss two sessions or clearly state that they wish to quit. When clients return after an absence, they are urged to make future attendance a priority and to make whatever arrangements are necessary to avoid further absences.

Lateness

Therapists should convey the attitude that sessions are too important to waste time by being late and should make reasonable efforts to help clients solve whatever problems may be causing them to be late.

If a client is less than 15–20 minutes late, the session should take place and end at the regularly scheduled time. If a client is more than 25 minutes late, the therapist should attempt to reschedule within the next few days.

Extra Sessions

Some patients will request extra session with the therapist, particularly in the early weeks of treatment. The need for extra sessions should be determined by the clinical judgment of the therapist, based on the seriousness of the situation. The maximum number of permissible extra sessions in the Project MATCH protocol is two (making the maximum number of sessions 14). If a patient requires more than two additional sessions with the therapist, the possibility of clinical deterioration and/or withdrawal from the study is considered.

Concurrent Treatment

In Project MATCH, certain limitations are placed on participation in other forms of therapy during the 12-week intervention period. Since 12-step treatment is another modality in this clinical trial, therapists in the cognitive-behavioral modality are instructed to assume a neutral stance toward clients' participation in 12-step fellowship activities. Attendance at Alcoholics Anonymous (AA) is neither encouraged nor discouraged. If therapists have difficulty with this requirement, they discuss their concerns at once with their project coordinator, supervisor, or training staff.

In addition, Project MATCH clients may not be seen by other mental health professionals for more than a total of 6 contact hours during their 12 weeks of treatment in the study. If clients express interest in other forms of treatment, they are urged to postpone them, if possible, until after this treatment is completed.

Clinical Deterioration

Criteria have been developed to define clinical deterioration. All instances must be reviewed with the project coordinator. These include development of acute psychosis, suicidal or homicidal ideation, onset of cognitive impairment, deterioration of physical health, and extensive drinking or drug use. Project MATCH has developed procedures for responding to these developments, and therapists are instructed to review them with the project coordinator at the first indication of a problem.

Termination

Termination can be problematic for many clients, and can lead to clinical deterioration or acting out prior to the end of treatment. About 4–5 weeks before the end of treatment, therapists should review the session on termination to sensitize themselves to the issues involved and to ensure that they respond to them in a manner consistent with this manual.

Core Sessions

In order to provide patients with effective cognitive-behavioral coping skills, therapists need to be sure to cover all eight core topics and to do so thoroughly. "Introduction" must be presented first, and the final session in the 12-week intervention must be "Termination." The remaining core topics can be discussed in any order. We suggest the sequence in which they are presented here:

Session 1: Introduction to Coping Skills Training

Session 2: Coping With Cravings and Urges to Drink

Session 3: Managing Thoughts About Alcohol and Drinking

Session 4: Problem Solving

Session 5: Drink Refusal Skills

Session 6: Planning for Emergencies and Coping With a Lapse

Session 7: Seemingly Irrelevant Decisions

After the first seven core sessions have been completed, the therapist may move on to one or more elective topics.

Final Session: Termination.

Session 1: Introduction to Coping Skills Training

This session has two major purposes: first, to establish rapport with the client, and second, to introduce the client to the reasoning behind coping skills training. By doing this, clients can have very clear expectations about how treatment will proceed and about what behaviors may be expected of them. The time shown for each topic area is only suggested, and some areas (e.g., building rapport) may take longer than the time shown, while others may require less.

Building Rapport (45 minutes)

This is an extremely important part of the treatment, where the therapist first gets to know the client. Therapists should begin by introducing themselves and by explaining who they are (e.g., a private practitioner in the area, a VA psychologist). The therapist should then explain the purpose of this first meeting: to get to know the client, to get an idea of the client's drinking patterns and motivation, and to discuss the rationale for treatment and what the sessions will be like. The initial interview should be informal, but it is desirable to obtain some key information in the first session. Questions to be asked of the client include the following (not necessarily in this order):

- Tell me a bit about yourself. What do you do for a living? Married? How do you spend your free time? What is your living situation like (lives alone, apartment, own house, children, extended family)?

- How serious do you think your drinking problem is?

- Why are you seeking treatment now?

- Why did you seek treatment here? How did you hear about this treatment program?

- Have you been treated before for alcoholism or drug abuse? (If yes: What were your experiences like?)

- Have you ever tried to quit on your own? (If yes: How did you do?)

- When you think about alcoholism treatment, what do you think about? That is, what is your idea of what treatment should be like?

- What do you want out of treatment? How will you get it?

- How confident are you that you can succeed, that is, remain abstinent?

Conceptualizing Treatment: What Is Alcoholism? (5 minutes)

Having begun to establish rapport with the client, therapists may begin to explain the rationale for coping-skills training. This begins with a social learning explanation of alcohol abuse. As therapists go through this explanation, they may illustrate the various points by drawing on what the client has already described. The explanation may run as follows:

In thinking about alcoholism, we view excessive drinking as harmful *behavior*. Once people start to drink alcohol a lot, they sometimes learn that it changes the way they feel. For example, some people use it like a tranquilizer to help them deal with stressful situations. Other people expect that it will make good times seem even better. Some people think it will make them more confident. Some people use it just to keep from thinking about things.

After a while, drinking can be triggered by things in the environment, sometimes without the person even realizing it. Often, things in the environment can trigger feelings of craving, but that does not happen with everyone. Things in the environment that often trigger drinking may include seeing alcoholic drinks, being in the presence of people who are drinking, or being in situations that are stressful.

Finally, people often develop beliefs about alcohol and about their own drinking (e.g., "Drinking is not a problem for me. I can stop whenever I want." "I need to change, but it's not worth the effort." "Stopping drinking is not possible for me.").

Alcohol can change the way a person feels, thinks, and acts. This can make substance abuse very easy to start and very difficult to stop. The purpose of this treatment is to help you avoid or cope better with those situations in which you tend to drink and to help you find behaviors that you can do instead of drinking.

The therapist should probe for understanding.

Assessing High-Risk Situations (15 minutes)

The therapist should give a brief explanation of how treatment works, again capitalizing on the client's experiences to make points more clearly.

> If drinking changes the way a person acts, thinks, and feels, we need to begin by finding out what situations you are most likely to drink in and what you are thinking and feeling in those situations. We call these high-risk situations. What we want to find out is what kinds of things are triggering or maintaining your drinking. Then we can try to develop other ways you can deal with high-risk situations without drinking. This involves learning specific skills and strategies to use.
>
> The main point is that once we know about the situations and problems that contribute to your drinking, we can look for other ways to deal with those situations.

The therapist should again probe for understanding or resistance.

Having given the client a rationale for treatment, the therapist should begin an informal assessment of high-risk situations. Among the questions the therapist might ask are—

- In what kinds of situations do you drink? What are your triggers for drinking?

- Can you give a specific example (e.g., a relapse story)?

- Can you remember your thoughts and feelings at the time?

- What were the positive consequences of drinking?

- What were the negative consequences of drinking?

The therapist should show the client the self-monitoring record handout and demonstrate its use by recording the above responses on it. The therapist should summarize with the client the apparent determinants of drinking in this episode and follow up by asking for other examples.

Motivation (5 minutes)

At this point, if clients are sufficiently engaged, the therapist can try to boost motivation by expressing confidence in their ability to do well in treatment. The therapist may also help the client review reasons to stop drinking and may elicit examples of the client's successes in the past (e.g., longest period of abstinence or controlled drinking to date). The therapist should commend the patient for making this effort now.

Contract and Ground Rules (10 minutes)

The therapist needs to stress at this point that treatment can help but that it will require certain commitments on the part of the client. The therapist will be there to help the client figure out how to deal with alcohol problems, but the client will have to work at it. That work will include certain ground rules:

- *Attendance.* The client must attend without fail. Cancellations must be made in advance, and the client must have a good reason to cancel. The client may withdraw from treatment but must discuss this decision with the therapist first (i.e., not just fail to show up).

- *Promptness.* The client must be on time for sessions. If for some reason clients cannot be on time on a given day, they must contact the therapist to that effect.

- *Alcohol and drug use.* This treatment is intended for people who want to abstain from alcohol. Although clients may not want to have total abstinence as the goal, they must work on remaining abstinent for the program to be most effective.

- *Completion of homework.* One of the ways in which this treatment works is that therapist and client decide the appropriate skills to learn and how best to learn them. This may include homework assignments, such as practicing specific skills, that clients must do if they are to benefit from treatment. The client, therefore, must agree to complete homework assignments.

These ground rules are set out in a contract that the therapist asks the client to read and sign. Included in the contract is a statement of the short-term goals that the client agrees to work on.

Homework (5 minutes)

The therapist sends the client home with the self-monitoring record, gives instructions in its use, and requests that the patient take time once a day to record episodes of craving or desire for alcohol. The therapist then sets the next appointment.

Treatment Contract

1. I understand that this treatment will last 12 weeks, and I agree to participate for that length of time. If I want to withdraw from the program, I agree to discuss this decision with my therapist prior to taking this action.

2. I agree to attend all sessions and to be prompt. If it is absolutely necessary that I cancel a session, I will call in advance to reschedule. I also agree to call in advance if I will be late to a session.

3. I understand that this treatment is intended for people who want to abstain from drugs and alcohol. I understand that I must work on remaining abstinent for this program to be most effective.

4. I agree that it is essential for me to come to the session drug and alcohol free. I understand that I will be asked to leave any session to which I come after using drugs or alcohol. I will be asked to arrange safe transportation home.

5. I understand that I will be expected to practice and implement some of the skills I discuss in treatment. I agree to bring in the practice exercise sheet each week to discuss with my therapist.

6. I agree to work on the following specific goals during the next 12 weeks.

   1. _____

   2. _____

   3. _____

- -

I have reviewed the above statements with my therapist, and we both agree to abide by them.

_____   _____
                                                  Date

_____   _____
                                                  Date

Self-Monitoring Record

TRIGGER (What sets me up to use?)	THOUGHTS AND FEELINGS (What was I thinking? What was I feeling?)	BEHAVIOR (What did I do then?)	POSITIVE CONSEQUENCES (What positive thing happened?)	NEGATIVE CONSEQUENCES (What negative thing happened?)

Reprinted with permission from Jaffe et al. 1988.

Session 2: Coping With Cravings and Urges to Drink

Rationale

1. Craving is most often experienced early in treatment, but episodes of craving may persist for weeks, months, and sometimes even years after some alcoholics stop drinking. Craving may be uncomfortable but is a very common experience and does not mean something is wrong. You should expect craving to occur from time to time and be prepared to cope with it if and when it occurs.

2. Urges to drink, or cravings, can be triggered by things you see in the *environment* that remind you of using alcohol. *Physical signs* may include tightness in your stomach or feeling nervous through your body; *psychological signs* may include increased thoughts of how good you would like to feel from using alcohol or drugs, remembering times you used alcohol in the past, planning how you would go about getting a drink, or feeling you need alcohol.

3. Craving and urges are time-limited, that is, they usually last only a few minutes and at most a few hours. Rather than increasing steadily until they become unbearable, they usually peak after a few minutes and then die down, like a wave. Urges will become less frequent and less intense as you learn how to cope with them.

Skill Guidelines

1. Learn how to recognize urge "triggers" so you can reduce your exposure to them.

   a. Common triggers include—

      - Exposure to alcohol itself.

      - Seeing other people drinking.

      - Contact with people, places, times of day, and situations commonly associated with drinking (such as drinking buddies, parties and bars, getting home from work, weekends).

      - Particular types of emotions (such as frustration, fatigue, feeling stressed out). Even positive emotions (elation, excitement, feelings of accomplishment) can be triggers.

– Physical feelings (feeling sick, shaky, tense).

b. Some triggers are hard to recognize, and self-monitoring, which will be assigned as the practice exercise this week, can help you recognize them.

c. The easiest way to deal with cravings and urges is to try to avoid them in the first place. This can be done by reducing your exposure to craving triggers (getting rid of alcohol in the house, not going to parties or bars, reducing contact with friends who drink, and so on).

2. Sometimes craving cannot be avoided, and it is necessary to find a way to cope with it. There are many different strategies for coping with craving:

a. *Get involved in some distracting activity.* Reading, a hobby, going to a movie, exercising (jogging, biking) are good examples of distracting activities. Once you get interested in something else, you'll find the urges go away. Another effective response to craving is eating, as most people do not feel like drinking after eating a big meal or something very sweet.

b. *Talk it through.* Talk to friends or family members about craving when it occurs. Talking about cravings and urges can be very helpful in pinpointing the source of the craving. Also, talking about craving often helps to discharge and relieve the feeling and will help restore honesty in your relationship. Craving is nothing to feel bad about.

c. *Urge surf.* Many people try to cope with their urges by gritting their teeth and toughing it out. Some urges, especially when you first return to your old drinking environment, are just too strong to ignore. When this happens, it can be useful to stay with your urge to drink until it passes. This technique is called *urge surfing.*

Urges are a lot like ocean waves. They are small when they start, grow in size, and then break up and dissipate. You can imagine yourself as a surfer who will ride the wave, staying on top of it until it crests, breaks, and turns into less powerful, foamy surf. The idea behind urge surfing is similar to the idea behind many martial arts. In judo, one overpowers an opponent by first *going with* the force of the attack. By joining with the opponent's force, one can take control of it and redirect it to one's advantage. This technique of gaining control by first going with the opponent also allows one to take control while expending minimal energy. Urge surfing is similar. You can initially join with an urge (as opposed to meeting it with a strong *opposing* force) as a way of taking control of it. After you have practiced urge surfing several times and become familiar with it, you may find it a useful technique when you have a strong urge to drink.

There are three basic steps in urge surfing:

1. Take an inventory of how you experience the craving. Do this by sitting in a comfortable chair with your feet flat on the floor and your hands in a comfortable position. Take a few deep breaths and focus your attention inward. Allow your attention to wander through your body. Notice where in your body you experience the craving and what the sensations are like. Notice each area where you experience the urge, and tell yourself what you are experiencing. For example, "Let me see . . . My craving is in my mouth and nose and in my stomach."

2. Focus on one area where you are experiencing the urge. Notice the exact sensations in that area. For example, do you feel hot, cold, tingly, or numb? Are your muscles tense or relaxed? How large an area is involved? Notice the sensations and describe them to yourself. Notice the changes that occur in the sensation. "Well, my mouth feels dry and parched. There is tension in my lips and tongue. I keep swallowing. As I exhale, I can imagine the smell and tingle of booze."

3. Repeat the focusing with each part of your body that experiences the craving. Pay attention to and describe to yourself the changes that occur in the sensations. Notice how the urge comes and goes. Many people, when they urge surf, notice that after a few minutes the craving has vanished. The purpose of this exercise, however, is not to make the craving go away but to experience the craving in a new way. If you practice urge surfing, you will become familiar with your cravings and learn how to ride them out until they go away naturally.

d. *Challenge and change your thoughts.* When experiencing a craving, many people have a tendency to remember only the positive effects of alcohol and often forget the negative consequences of drinking. Therefore, when experiencing craving, many people find it helpful to remind themselves of the benefits of not drinking and the negative consequences of drinking. This way, you can remind yourself that you really *won't* "feel better if you just have one drink," and that you stand to lose a lot by drinking. Sometimes it is helpful to have these benefits and consequences listed on a small card that you can keep with you.

People constantly appraise and think about things that happen to them and the things that they do. The way that you feel and act can be highly influenced by these subjective facts or appraisals as well as objective facts. What you tell yourself about your urges to drink will affect how you experience and handle them. Your self-talk can be put to use to strengthen or weaken your urges. The process of making self-statements becomes so automatic by the time you are an adult, you may not notice that you do this; it simply does not require any attention now. A self-statement that has become automatic for you is, "The big hand is on the 7, so it is 35 minutes after. The little hand is between the 2 and 3, so it is 2 o'clock. That means that the time is 2:35." Instead, you automatically read the clock to tell time. Hidden or automatic self-statements about urges can make them harder to handle ("Now I want a drink. I won't be able to stand this. The urge is going to keep getting stronger and stronger until I blow up or drink.") Other types of self-statements can make the urge easier to handle ("Even though my mind is made up to stay sober, my body will take a while to learn this too. This urge is uncomfortable, but in 15 minutes or so, I'll be feeling like myself again.").

There are two basic steps in using self-talk constructively:

1. Pinpoint what you tell yourself about an urge that makes it harder to cope with the urge. One way to tell if you are on the right track is when you hit upon a self-statement that increases your discomfort. That discomfort-raising self-statement is a leading suspect for challenge, since it pushes your buttons.

2. Use self-talk constructively to challenge that statement. An effective challenge will make you feel better (less tense, anxious, panicky) even though it may not make the feelings disappear entirely. The most effective challenges are ones that are tailored to your specific upsetting self-statements. Listed below are some stock challenges that people find useful:

   What is the evidence? What is the evidence that if you don't have a drink in the next 10 minutes, you will die? Has anyone (who has been detoxed) ever died from not drinking? What's the evidence that people who are recovering from an alcohol problem don't experience the feelings that you have? What is the evidence that there is something the matter with you, that you will never improve?

What is so awful about that? What's so awful about feeling bad? Of course you can survive it. Who said that sobriety would be easy? What's so terrible about experiencing an urge? If you hang in there, you will feel fine. These urges are *not* like being hungry or thirsty or needing to relieve yourself—they are more like a craving for food or an urge to talk to a particular person—they pass, in time.

You are a regular human being and have a right to make mistakes. Maybe you worry about being irritable, preoccupied, or hard to get along with. What's so bad about that? We all make mistakes, and in a situation that is complicated, there is no right or perfect way to get along. Our most memorable lessons, invariably, are learned in the school of hard knocks. It's a school that every single one of us attends throughout life.

Some of the substitute thoughts or self-statements will only be necessary or helpful initially, as ways of distracting yourself from persistent urges; you'll have an easier time if you replace the uncomfortable thoughts with other activities. After a while, sobriety will feel less unnatural; many of the urges will diminish and drop out, and you won't need constant replacements.

In-Session Exercises

1. Make a list of craving triggers. Circle the triggers that you can avoid or to which you can reduce your exposure (like not having alcohol in your home).

2. Make up a craving plan. Pick two or three of the general strategies that were discussed and make up a plan about how you would put them into practice if you experience an urge. Remember—cravings can come when you least expect them! For example, if you think getting involved in a distracting activity would be helpful, which activities would you pick? Are these available to you now? Which may take some preparation? If you were feeling craving, who would be best for you to call? If you have not tried urge surfing before, it might be very helpful to practice with your therapist before trying it when facing an urge.

Coping with Cravings and Urges

Reminder Sheet

- Urges are common in the recovery process. They are not a sign of failure. Instead, try to learn from them about what your craving triggers are.

- Urges are like ocean waves. They get stronger only to a point, then they start to go away.

- You win every time you defeat an urge by not using. Urges only get stronger if you give in and feed them. An urge will eventually weaken and die if you do not feed it.

Practice Exercises

For next week, make a daily record of urges to use drugs or drink, the intensity of those urges, and the coping behaviors you used.

1. Fill out the DAILY RECORD OF URGES TO DRINK

   a. *Date*

   b. *Situation*: Include anything about the situation or your thoughts or feelings that seemed to trigger the urge to drink.

   c. *Intensity of thirst*: Rate your thirst, where 1 = none at all, 100 = worst ever.

   d. *Coping behavior*: Use this column to note how you attempted to cope with the urge to drink. If it seems like it would help, note the effectiveness of your coping.

2. Below is an example of how to fill out the record form.

DAILY RECORD OF URGES TO DRINK

Date	Situation (include your thoughts and feelings)	Intensity of cravings (1–100)	Coping behaviors used
5/16/91	Was feeling stressed. Had a disagreement with my boss.	75	Shut myself in office and relaxed. Felt better after 20 minutes
5/17/91	Antsy at bed time. Trouble getting ready to go to bed.	60	Took a hot shower, listened to the relaxation tape. Shower better than tape.
5/18/91	Went to Andy's Diner for lunch, where I always used to order something to drink.	80	Ordered tonic with lime. It was a close call. Should have prepared in advance.
5/19/91	Pay day. Bob wanted to party after work.	68	Suggested we go for coffee. Bob agreed. Boy—was I surprised!

Daily Record of Urges to Drink

Date	Situation (include your thoughts and feelings)	Intensity of cravings (1–100)	Coping behaviors used

Session 3: Managing Thoughts About Alcohol and Drinking

Rationale

The following paragraph is inserted between the first and second elements of the Monti et al. rationale:

> Recovering alcoholics need to be aware of a state of mind that can predispose them to a relapse—a state of mind characterized by certain dangerous attitudes and thought processes. This state of mind is often described as *"negative tapes."* These thought processes and attitudes are dangerous because they induce alcoholics to relax their guard (decrease vigilance). Stinking thinking, as the saying goes, leads to drinking thinking, and then, usually, to drinking without thinking. It is not the thinking itself that creates the problem, but how people deal with it. If alcoholics can learn to dismiss this thinking from their minds whenever it appears, recognize it for what it is, or counter it with contrary thoughts, it need not lead to a relapse.

The following items are added to the list of situations that may lead clients to have thoughts about resuming drinking:

f. *Escape.* Individuals wish to avoid the discomfort aroused by unpleasant situations, conflicts, or memories. Failure, rejection, disappointment, hurt, humiliation, embarrassment, discontent, or sadness all tend to demand relief. People get tired of feeling hassled, lousy, and upset. They just want to get away from it all and, more to the point, from themselves. It is not necessarily intoxication that is sought; rather it is numbness, the absence of problems, and peace.

g. *Relaxation.* Thoughts of wanting to unwind are perfectly normal, but they go awry when they are coupled with the

NOTE: The major portion of this session is based on the corresponding session in Monti et al. (pp. 79–83). A number of additions made to the original materials are derived from Ludwig (1988). © Oxford University Press. Used with permission.

expectations of this happening immediately, without the benefit of doing something relaxing. Rather than engaging in a wide variety of possibly enjoyable and relaxing activities, the individual may choose the more immediate route induced through alcohol.

h. *Socialization*. This overlaps with relaxation but is confined to social situations. Many individuals, shy or uncomfortable in social settings, may feel a need for a social lubricant to feel more at ease and decrease the awkwardness and inhibitions they feel around others.

i. *Improved self-image*. This situation typically involves a relatively pervasive negative and low self-esteem. When individuals start becoming unhappy with themselves, when they are feeling inferior to others, when they regard themselves as lacking in essential qualities, when they feel unattractive or deficient, they often begin to think again of alcohol, through which they may have previously achieved immediate and temporary relief.

j. *Romance*. Individuals often indulge in adolescent fantasies. When bored or unhappy with their lives, they yearn for excitement, romance, the joy of flirtation, and the thrill of being in love. This is usually the kind of thought that, when engaged in too seriously, requires a drug like alcohol to sustain it and make it more vivid and real.

k. *To hell with it*. Some individuals seem to have lost all incentive for pursuing any worthwhile goals. Their thoughts express disillusionment; nothing really matters. There is no reason to try. Why should they give a damn? Such an attitudinal set leads these individuals to be less vigilant and not care whether they remain sober.

l. *No control*. This represents the other side of the coin from the "Testing Control" script. Just as believing in one's ability to handle alcohol is usually a setup for relapse, the opposite attitude of not being able to control one's cravings virtually insures it. Individuals give up the fight, conceding defeat even before they have made any effort to resist. Alcohol is seen as one of the few viable options available. This differs from the "hell with it" attitude. In that situation, individuals do not necessarily feel powerless; they just do not want to exert the effort to continue what they have been doing.

Skill Guidelines

The following introductory paragraph is added:

All recovering people have thoughts about drinking at one time or another. The thinking itself does not create the problem, but how people deal with it. If alcoholics can learn to dismiss this thinking from their minds whenever it appears, recognize it for what it is, or counter it with contrary thoughts, it need not lead to a relapse. There are three general and overriding prerequisites for an individual to cope effectively with thoughts about drinking: (1) one needs to be firmly committed to recovery in order to choose to remain abstinent and not give in to persistent thoughts; (2) one must be aware of the persistent aspects of thinking that would allow the individual to rationalize and justify (and provide guilt-free) drinking; (3) one must maintain a high level of vigilance, always anticipating potential risks to relapse and never assuming that one is immune from the prospect of giving into urges, cravings, or thoughts of drinking.

Add the following paragraph after the first skill guideline:

An important aspect of challenging possible thoughts about drinking (as well as forms of thought distraction and substitute behaviors incompatible with drinking) is *not* to visualize what one is *not* going to do but to picture a substitute or opposing behavior that one *is* going to do. To begin a new habit, individuals should have a behavioral image of themselves engaging in the new behavior, not just on occasion but every time the unwanted habit pops into mind.

The following paragraph is added after the third skill guideline:

The individual is asked to think beyond the more immediate pleasure associated with alcohol, to play out the mental image of the possible drinking episode to the end, and to include all the detrimental consequences that could arise if drinking occurs.

In skill guideline number 8, the reference to calling one's AA sponsor is eliminated in Project MATCH to reduce overlap with the 12-Step facilitation treatment.

Introducing the Practice Exercise

The practice exercise in Monti et al. has been modified somewhat. The following paragraph replaces the one on page 83 in Monti et al.:

Ask clients to write out lists of (1) the 5 to 10 most anticipated positive consequences of sobriety and not drinking, (2) the 5 to 10 most negative personal consequences associated with drinking, and (3) the 5 to 10 greatest stumbling blocks or high-risk situations that will make it difficult to achieve or maintain sobriety. Then, ask clients to use this information (the positive benefits of sobriety and the negative consequences of drinking) to rate how committed they are to stop using and to stay sober. The rating of the person's perceived level of commitment ranges from 1 (no commitment) to 10 (extremely high level of commitment).

Practice Exercise

The following composite Practice Exercise incorporates the modifications to the one in Monti et al.:

One way to cope with thoughts about using alcohol is to remind yourself of the benefits of not using, the unpleasant consequences of using, and the stumbling blocks or high-risk situations that may make it hard to keep your commitment to abstinence. Use this sheet to make a list of the 5 to 10 reminders in each category, then transfer this list onto a pocket-sized index card. Read this card whenever you start to have thoughts about drinking.

Positive benefits of not using: _____

_____

_____

_____

Unpleasant effects or negative consequences of using: _____

_____

_____

_____

Stumbling blocks, or high-risk situations, to keeping commitment to

abstinence: _____

_____

_____

_____

Overall level of personal commitment to remain abstinent:

None   1   2   3   4   5   6   7   8   9   10   Extremely high

Session 4: Problem Solving

This session is based on the similar one in Monti et al., pages 83–87, with the following modifications.

Rationale

Item 2 of the Monti et al. rationale section is replaced with the following:

2. Alcohol and drug abusers are likely to encounter the following general types of problems:

   a. Situations where drinking and drug use has occurred in the past

   b. Situations that arise only after you have stopped drinking or using drugs (i.e., social pressure, cravings, and slips)

   c. Difficulty in developing activities that may be useful to maintain sobriety (e.g., new recreational habits)

   What sort of problems have you encountered so far?

Skill Guidelines

Items 3b and 3c are dropped and replaced with the following:

   b. Consider both *behavioral* and *cognitive* coping strategies (Sanchez-Craig 1983). When a problem involves conflict with other people, it is often better to employ behavioral coping and speak up (in an assertive way) so as to change the situation for the better. Negative emotional reactions to uncontrollable events may be best handled with cognitive coping, changing the way you think about the situation. In this manner, you may reduce your negative emotional reaction without changing a situation that may be beyond your control. In some situations, both cognitive and behavioral coping strategies are necessary to deal with a problem.

Behavior Rehearsal Role Plays

Retain the first paragraph in Monti et al., but omit the subsequent group exercises.

Reminder Sheet and Practice Exercise

These are retained as in Monti et al., page 212.

Session 5: Drink Refusal Skills

The majority of this session is based on the corresponding session in Monti et al., pages 61–63. The following changes have been made.

Rationale

Item 2 in Monti et al. is added to item 4. The following two elements are inserted in place of the relocated item 2:

> As drinking increases in severity over time, there appears to be a "funneling" effect or narrowing of social relationships: individuals begin to eliminate sober friends, and their peer group becomes populated with others who support and reinforce continued drinking. Being with such individuals and former drinking buddies increases the risk of relapse through multiple avenues: (1) overt and covert pressure to drink; (2) conditioned craving associated with people, places, activities, and emotional states related to past drinking; (3) increased positive outcome expectancies about the effects of drinking; and (4) increased access/availability of substances.

> Two forms of social/peer pressure are often experienced by individuals in recovery: direct and indirect social pressure. The former occurs when someone offers the individual a drink directly and up front. This is most likely to happen in high-risk situations. Indirect social pressure involves returning to the same old settings (e.g., taverns, lounges, parties), with the same people, doing the same things, and experiencing the same feelings previously associated with drinking.

The following is added at the beginning of item 3 in the Monti et al. rationale:

> Given the increased risk associated with social pressure, the first action that should be considered is behavioral avoidance. However, avoidance is not always possible or practical.

Skill Guidelines

The following paragraph is added at the beginning of the skill guidelines section:

If unable to avoid high-risk situations and people, the next level of response is being able to refuse requests to drink. The more rapidly a person is able to say "no" to such requests, the less likely he/she is to relapse. Why is this so? The old notion of "he who hesitates is lost"; that is, being unsure and hesitant allows you to begin rationalizing (e.g., "One beer wouldn't be so bad."). The goal then is to learn to say "no" in a convincing manner and to have your response at the tip of your tongue.

In-Session Practice

The following material is added prior to the Modeling exercise. It requires having available the "Drinking Locations" and the "Social Situations" cards from the "Comprehensive Drinker Profile" (Miller and Marlatt 1984).[2]

Provide the clients with the "Drinking Locations" cards from the "Comprehensive Drinker Profile." Have them sort the cards from the most to the least frequent drinking setting. This listing of drinking settings will enable the client to anticipate settings having high risk for drinking and social pressure to drink.

Next, provide the clients with the "Social Situations" cards from the "Comprehensive Drinker Profile." Have them sort the cards from the most to the least frequent drinking situation. Have the clients indicate which of the people identified in their social network they anticipate contacting during the next 90 days. Ask them to indicate which of these individuals are likely to support sobriety and which are likely to tempt/pressure them to drink.

This exercise will help clients identify people and situations to avoid because they represent a high risk to their sobriety. It will also help the therapist identify specific individuals and situations to include in the behavioral rehearsal role play.

Modeling

The therapist plays the role of the person being pressured to drink (by the client) and demonstrates an effective and assertive way to handle the situation.

Behavioral Rehearsal Role Play

This is conducted essentially the same way as described in Monti et al. An additional source of ideas for role plays derives from the in-session practice exercise: those locations and situations that were identified as high frequency represent considerable risk and would therefore provide good scenarios for role playing. The following suggestions are added at the end of the Role Play section:

2 Miller, W.R., and Marlatt, G.A. *Comprehensive Drinker Profile*. Odessa, FL: Psychological Assessment Resources, Inc., 1984.

- The therapist should encourage the client to try to visualize scenarios involving a group of people, even though the individual therapy situation does not provide an opportunity for the use of multiple role-play partners.

- In many cases, it may be useful for the therapist to elicit the client's fantasies about how the target person will react to the client's refusal to drink.

Reminder Sheets and Practice Exercises

These are retained as in Monti et al., page 205.

Session 6: Planning for Emergencies and Coping With a Lapse

This session is based almost entirely on the similar session in Monti et al. entitled "Planning for Emergencies" (pp. 120–121). The Project MATCH manual included a few modifications, as follows.

Rationale

The fifth item in the Monti et al. rationale section is replaced by the following two items:

5. If a lapse or slip back to drinking does occur, it is likely to be accompanied by feelings of guilt and shame. These must be dealt with at once, before they lead to further drinking. After a slip, one should try to learn, from the events that preceded it, to reduce the likelihood of a repetition.

6. Ask the client to describe one or more life events or life changes that might lead to craving for alcohol or to a lapse. The therapist should list these on the chalkboard and ask clients to consider how they might affect their behavior and interactions with others.

Skill Guidelines

Two additional skill guidelines items have been added. These are taken from page 157 of Monti et al., the paragraphs on dealing with the immediate aftermath and the longer term impact of a drinking episode.

Practice Exercise

The practice exercise remains as specified in Monti et al.

Reminder Sheets

Two reminder sheets from Jaffe et al. (1988) have been added. These are reproduced below.

Personal Emergency Plan: High-Risk Situation

Reminder Sheet

If I encounter a life event that puts me in a high-risk situation:

1. I will leave or change the situation or environment.

2. I will put off the decision to drink for 15 minutes. I will remember that most cravings are time-limited and I can wait it out—not drink.

3. I will challenge my thoughts about drinking. Do I really need a drink? I will remind myself that my only true needs are for air, water, food, and shelter.

4. I will think of something unrelated to drinking.

5. I will remind myself of my successes to this point.

6. I will call my list of emergency numbers:

NAME	PHONE NUMBER
1. _____	_____
2. _____	_____
3. _____	_____
4. _____	_____
5. _____	_____
6. _____	_____

GOOD LUCK!

REMEMBER: RIDING OUT THIS CRISIS WILL STRENGTHEN YOUR RECOVERY

Personal Emergency Plan: Lapse

Reminder Sheet

A slip is a major crisis in recovery. Returning to abstinence will require an all-out effort. Here are some things that can be done.

If I experience a lapse:

1. I will get rid of the alcohol and get away from the setting where I lapsed.

2. I will realize that one drink or even one day of drinking/drug use does not have to result in a full blown relapse. I will not give in to feelings of guilt or blame because I know these feelings will pass in time.

3. I will call for help from someone else.

4. At my next session, I will examine this lapse with my therapist, discuss the events prior to my lapse, and identify triggers and my reaction to them. I will explore with my therapist what I expected alcohol to change or provide. I will work with my therapist to set up a plan so that I will be able to cope with a similar situation in the future.

REMEMBER: THIS LAPSE IS ONLY A TEMPORARY DETOUR ON THE ROAD TO ABSTINENCE

Session 7: Seemingly Irrelevant Decisions

The goals of this session are to (1) convey to the client the kinds of seemingly irrelevant thoughts, behaviors, and decisions that may culminate in a high-risk situation and (2) encourage the client to articulate and think through all decisions, no matter how small, in order to avoid rationalizations or minimizations of risk (e.g., "I need to keep a few beers in the refrigerator in case my brother-in-law comes over.").

Material for this session was taken from Monti et al., pages 116–120, with a few modifications.

Rationale

Marlatt and Gordon's (1985, p. 273) "George the Drinker" story is substituted for the "Sam the Gambler" story on pages 117–118 because of its more direct link to drinking.

The following is added to point 3 on page 117:

> By paying more attention to the decisionmaking process, you will have a greater chance to interrupt the chain of decisions that could lead to a relapse. This is important because it is much easier to stop the process early, before you wind up in a high-risk situation, than later when you are in a situation that is harder to handle and may expose you to a number of triggers.
>
> Also, by paying attention to your decisionmaking process, you will be able to recognize certain kinds of thoughts that can lead to making risky decisions, such as George's thought that he "had to" have a cigarette in the story ("George the Drinker"). Thoughts like "I have to" go to a party, "should" see a certain drinking buddy, or "have to" drive by a particular place, often occur at the beginning of a Seemingly Irrelevant Decision and should be treated as a warning or red flag. Other red-flag thoughts often start with "It doesn't matter if I . . . ," "I can handle . . . ," and so on.

Group Discussion

This exercise is easily accomplished in the individual therapy setting. The item referring to AA or Narcotics Anonymous meetings is omitted in Project MATCH.

Exercise in Group

This too is easily adapted to individual therapy. The following exercises are added:

- Think about the most recent time you drank. Trace back through the decisionmaking chain. What was the starting point (exposure to a trigger, certain thoughts)? Can you recognize the choice points where you made risky decisions?

- What plans have you made for this weekend? If none, why? Is this a seemingly irrelevant decision? Sometimes *not planning* means *planning to drink*. What plans could you make for this weekend that would reduce the risk of winding up in a risky situation?

Final Core Session: Termination

This session is based on materials from two sections in Monti et al. It begins with material from chapter 4, pages 160–161, the subheadings entitled "Termination," "Considering the Need for More Treatment," and "Planning for Emergencies," with material on taking Antabuse and attending AA deleted. The session description then picks up two subheadings from the session "Wrap-Up and Goodbyes," page 124: "Feedback to the Therapists" and "Goodbyes." The session description concludes with "Coping With Persistent Problems," pages 161–162.

Elective Sessions

Therapists may present up to four elective sessions after the first seven core sessions. The therapist and client should agree on which sessions to use. If the therapist feels that a particular session is especially relevant to a client, but the client disagrees, it is probably better to go along with the client's choice.

The sessions listed here can be offered in any order.

Starting Conversations

Nonverbal Communication

Introduction to Assertiveness

Receiving Criticism

Awareness of Anger

Anger Management

Awareness of Negative Thinking

Managing Negative Thinking

Increasing Pleasant Activities

Managing Negative Moods and Depression

Enhancing Social Support Networks

Job-Seeking Skills

Couples/Family Involvement I

Couples/Family Involvement II

Elective Session: Starting Conversations

This session is exactly as presented in Monti et al., pages 28–32. The only modification is elimination of the modeling section, which would require an interaction between cotherapists.

Elective Session: Nonverbal Communication

This session has no changes from the corresponding session in Monti et al., pages 35–40 except for minor modifications in wording to accomodate individually administered treatment.

Elective Session: Introduction to Assertiveness

The majority of this session is exactly as found in Monti et al., pages 46–49, with the few following changes.

Skill Guidelines

A 7th skill guideline is added:

7. Some of the most difficult situations in which to respond assertively are those that may potentially end with negative consequences. These often involve anticipatory anxiety, which can have a disorganizing effect. Examine the cognitions that may be preventing you from acting assertively (e.g., "I'll get fired if I tell my boss I can't work overtime tonight because I have to get to my therapy session"). In examining these cognitions, apply many of the same skills discussed for managing thoughts about drinking. These include:

   a. *Determine the thought or fear.* What's stopping me from asserting myself? What am I afraid will happen? What's the worst that could happen if I stand up for myself? What's so upsetting about that?

   b. *Assess the probabilities.* How likely is the negative consequence? (How likely is it that I get fired for not working overtime once?)

   c. *Evaluate the catastrophe.* What would happen if the dire consequence occurred? Would I be able to get another job? Would my life be over?

   d. *Identify the rules.* What assumptions and beliefs are governing my feelings in this situation? (Should I please everybody? Is it necessary that everyone like me?)

Behavior Reversal Role Play	Omit this exercise.

Modeling

Omit the Monti et al. modeling exercise and replace it with the following:

1. Have the client role play a coworker who suggests that the therapist accompany him/her for a drink after work. The therapist will model passive, aggressive, passive-aggressive, and assertive responses, respectively. After each type of response, ask the client to identify the type of behavior that was demonstrated and how successful each of the approaches would be in avoiding drinking.

2. Practicing assertive responses

   Have the client generate a number of situations that were difficult in the past (not necessarily those involving drinking) and practice assertive responses in role plays. If the client has trouble supplying these readily, try some easy ones (e.g., returning an item bought in a store to the clerk, dismissing a pesky salesperson) and some difficult ones (e.g., asking a good friend to return a loan made several months ago or confronting a supervisor who took credit for an idea of the client's).

Practice Exercise

If the response style in any of the three social situations specified in the Monti et al. exercise (p. 201) is not assertive, the client is asked to think of an assertive response and write it down.

Elective Session: Receiving Criticism

This session represents a combination of the two sessions in Monti et al. on "Receiving Criticism," pages 55–58, and "Receiving Criticism About Drinking," pages 58–61.

Rationale

Combine the two rationale sections from Monti et al. on pages 55–56 and 58–59.

Skill Guidelines

Combine the skill guidelines sections on pages 56–57 and 59.

Modeling

The modeling exercise from the "Receiving Criticism" session (p. 57) is utilized, with the client first playing the part of the critical store manager and the therapist modeling receipt of criticism in the role of clerk, followed by a role reversal.

Behavior Reversal Role Play

The behavior rehearsal role plays of both sessions are omitted in Project MATCH.

Practice Exercise

The practice exercises from both sessions are retained (pp. 203–204).

Elective Session: Awareness of Anger

This session has no changes from the corresponding session in Monti et al., pages 103–105, except for minor modifications in wording to accommodate individually administered treatment.

Elective Session: Anger Management

This session has no changes from the corresponding session in Monti et al., pages 106–108, except for minor modifications in wording to accommodate individually administered treatment.

Elective Session: Awareness of Negative Thinking

This session has no changes from the corresponding session in Monti et al., pages 108–111, except for minor modifications in wording to accommodate individually administered treatment.

Elective Session: Managing Negative Thinking

This session has no changes from the corresponding session in Monti et al., pages 111–116, except for minor modifications in wording to accommodate individually administered treatment.

Elective Session: Increasing Pleasant Activities

The goal of this session is to encourage the client to participate in activities which are pleasurable in order to provide a constructive behavioral alternative to alcohol use and to help the client counter the feelings of boredom and loneliness many problem drinkers experience when they stop drinking.

Material for this session was taken from pages 87–89 of the Monti et al. book, with the following modifications.

Skill Guidelines

Add to skill guideline number 1:

Try to think of some activities you would enjoy doing by yourself and some you would enjoy with other people. A balanced life includes both private time and social time. Asking others to participate in pleasant activities with you is a good ice breaker and another way to enlarge your circle of friends and supporters.

Add to skill guideline number 3:

Try to schedule this time during high-risk periods (e.g., after work, after dinner, on weekends). This way, you can reward yourself with positive activities rather than with drinking. Keeping yourself active with pleasant activities when you might be likely to think about drinking can result in your not thinking about drinking at all.

Add skill guideline number 5:

5. Also remember that getting involved with a pleasant activity is a great way to cope with cravings and urges.

Elective Session: Managing Negative Moods and Depression

Rationale

1. Negative moods and depression are common among alcoholics during the recovery process. Often, these moods are related to the actual depressant effects of alcohol or drugs or to the losses experienced in one's life (e.g., family, job, finances) as a result of drinking. Depression and negative moods related to these factors often get better during the course of treatment without any specific attention, as one is sober longer and begins to deal more effectively with the remaining life problems. Some people, however, continue to experience problems with depression even after they have been clean and sober for fairly long periods of time. In such cases, it may be necessary to focus more directly on these negative moods.

2. Depression is a problem in its own right. However, it is a particular problem for the recovering alcoholic, since negative mood states, particularly depression, are a major reason for relapse and, thus, represent high-risk situations.

3. Returning to drinking is not an effective way to cope with depression and only serves to make the person more depressed in the long run.

4. There are many different ways to cope with depression and negative moods. Given the focus of the present therapy approach, negative moods can be dealt with effectively by changing the ways one thinks and behaves. As such, many of the skills that have been learned to manage negative thoughts, to solve problems, and to increase pleasant activities can be used to deal with depression and its symptoms.

5. The best way to beat depression is to consider each symptom as a separate problem to be solved. The symptoms of depression are interrelated; improvement in one area leads to improvement in other areas.

NOTE: Adapted from Emery 1981. © Simon and Schuster. Used with permission.

Skill Guidelines

Depression has a number of causes and symptoms. Several different cognitive-behavioral approaches have been found helpful in dealing with depression of mild to moderate proportions.

1. *Change your way of thinking about yourself and the world.* One of the things that is most characteristic of depression is that the individual tends to view the world and the self through distorted and depressive perceptions. The way one thinks affects how one feels. As such, it is important to look at the way you think and see if this contributes to your feeling sad and depressed.

2. The steps to changing your thinking, while not easy, are simple. First, become *aware* of your self-defeating thoughts; second, *answer* these with more realistic ones; and third, *act* on the new thoughts. If you use these three *A's*, you can overcome the symptoms and causes of your depression.

3. *Awareness.* The first step in the process is to recognize the symptoms of your depression. Depressed people often miss or misinterpret symptoms of depression. Below are some ways you can become more aware of your symptoms:

    a. *Pay attention to your mood changes.* When you start to feel *sad, gloomy, ashamed, bored, lonely, or rejected,* tune into what's going on, to how you're feeling. These are important clues to your thinking.

    b. *Own your feelings.* If you are having trouble recognizing your feelings, start talking about them. Tell people how you are honestly feeling at any given moment.

    c. *Be alert to your body.* This is a clue to your emotions. Notice your posture, your facial expression, how you are walking and moving.

    d. *Label your avoidance.* Keep a lookout for people, places, and activities that you once enjoyed but are now avoiding. Forget about the reasons *why* you are avoiding them, just see *when* you do.

    e. *Watch for times when your confidence disappears.* Are there times and places when you ask others for help? Ask yourself whether you were able to handle this on your own before. Remember, this loss of confidence can be a symptom of depression.

f. *Look for activities that require great effort.* Do you have to force yourself to make or return phone calls? Do you have trouble completing tasks around the house?

g. *Become aware of trouble concentrating or making decisions.* Do you vacillate over simple decisions or second guess yourself? These can be symptoms of depression.

The second level of awareness is catching the thoughts that come before your symptoms. These are called *automatic negative thoughts.* During depression, these automatic negative thoughts become stronger and drown out more sensible thoughts. Thoughts are used to monitor feelings and behavior. They are used to initiate action and anticipate events. Your thoughts tell you what to do and how to feel. The chief characteristic of automatic negative thoughts is that *they are generally wrong.*

Automatic thoughts make you depressed; the more depressed you become, the more negative thoughts you will have and the more likely you are to believe them. Below is a list of thinking errors or methods of distortion characteristic of depressed thoughts.

Thinking Errors

Type of error	Examples
Personalizing	Thinking all situations and events revolve around you. "Everyone was looking at me and wondering why I was there."
Magnifying	Blowing negative events out of proportion. "This is the worst thing that could happen to me."
Minimizing	Glossing over the saving and positive factors. Overlooking the fact that "nothing really bad happened."
Either/or thinking	"Either I'm a loser or a winner." Not taking into account the full continuum.
Taking events out of context	After a successful interview, focusing on one or two tough questions. "I blew the interview."
Jumping to conclusions	"I have a swollen gland. This must be cancer."
Overgeneralizing	"I always fail—I fail at everything I ever try."
Self-blame	"I'm no good." Blaming total self rather than specific behaviors that can be changed.
Magical thinking	"Everything is bad because of my bad past deeds."

Mind reading	"Everyone there thought I was fat and ugly."
Comparing	Comparing self with someone else and ignoring all of the basic differences. "Cher has a better figure than mine."
Catastrophizing	Putting the worst possible construction on events. "I know something terrible happened."

In addition to becoming aware of the typical thoughts associated with depression noted above, it is important for you to become aware of *your* characteristic automatic negative thoughts. A number of steps can be taken to help you do this.

    a. *One way to become more aware of your thoughts is simply to count them*. This will help you realize that they just appear— they are automatic and not a reflection of reality.

    b. *Give yourself a goal of collecting 50 negative thoughts*. It seems like an impossible task, but it will prompt you to think hard and you are likely to come up with 5 to 10 such thoughts, even if you don't make it to 50!

    c. *Use an instant replay technique*. If you have some negative feelings and cannot quite catch the thoughts, replay the feelings over and over until you catch the thoughts. If you can remember what happened, imagine the event *as if* it were happening right now.

    d. *Look for the meaning of the situation*. Ask yourself, "What is the significance of the situation . . . what are the consequences?" By doing this you can usually become aware of your thoughts.

    e. *Set aside a specific time to collect negative thoughts*. You may find that setting aside a regular time may be helpful. During a half hour period, for example, write out some of the negative thoughts you had during the day. You might want to limit the thoughts to specific problems or situations.

    f. *Write out your thoughts*. Putting your thoughts down on paper is one of the best ways to become aware of them. When writing them out, force yourself to go beyond the obvious thoughts that first come to mind.

    g. *Use the excuses you come up with to avoid collecting negative thoughts as cues to swing into action*. This way the excuse can become an early warning signal.

    4. *Answering*. Once you begin catching negative thoughts, you can begin answering them. The secret to answering negative thoughts

is to realize there are different interpretations of any event and some are closer to reality than others. When answering your thoughts, try to consider a wide range of possible interpretations, not just the negative ones. If you are depressed, it is important to separate thoughts from facts, since you will have distorted thoughts, and when you believe and act on distorted thoughts, you become more depressed. You must begin to question the assumptions involved in the thoughts. A good way to do this is to ask some serious questions of yourself and your automatic thoughts.

Here are 20 questions that you can use to generate answers to your negative thoughts:

1. What's the evidence? Ask yourself, "Would this thought hold up in a court of law or is it circumstantial?" Just because the newspaper is late one day doesn't mean you can't count on anything. Give yourself a fair trial before you convict yourself.

2. Am I making a mistake in assuming what causes what? Determining causes is rarely simple. Example: Many women think they're fat because they have no willpower. Scientists have been studying obesity for years and they don't know what causes it. They know the determinants are partly biological, social, cultural, psychological, familial, and economic. Saying lack of willpower causes obesity is an oversimplification. Specifics are difficult to pinpoint.

3. Am I confusing a thought with a fact? This can lead to trouble—especially if you call yourself names and then believe them as gospel. There is an old story that makes this point: "How many legs would a dog have if you called the tail a leg? Five? Wrong. The answer is four. Calling a tail a leg doesn't make it so." Don't be dogmatic about your thoughts—look for the facts.

4. Am I close enough to the situation to really know what's happening? One woman said, "The bosses upstairs don't like our department's work and want to get rid of us." Who knows what they're thinking upstairs? You're not up there with them. You have to rely on what you know as fact. The woman's worry turned out to be a false rumor.

5. Am I thinking in all-or-none terms? Do you see the world in either/or terms ("I'm ugly and everyone else is beautiful")? Just about everything is in degrees and on a continuum. Even a person's gender is not always clear cut; some people's hormonal makeup is such that it's a tossup whether they're male or female.

6. Am I using ultimatum words in my thinking? ("I always should be nice or no one will like me.") You place unfair ultimatums on yourself with these words. This isn't "just semantics," but relates directly to how you feel and act.

7. Am I taking examples out of context? One student believed she'd been given a bad letter of recommendation. She thought the teacher said in the letter that she was narrow and rigid. When she reread the letter, she saw the teacher had written, "She has high principles." It was really a positive letter, and she had taken this part out of context.

8. Am I being honest with myself? Am I trying to fool myself—denying the truth, making excuses, and misplacing the blame? One depressed woman, speeding on the freeway, thought, "I hope they catch me and put me in jail." When she thought about it for a moment, she realized she didn't really mean this.

9. What is the source of my information? Consider your sources. People have their own reasons for what they tell you. "Am I depending on unreliable sources and spreaders of gloom to tell me how it is ? Why let them define reality for me?"

10. Am I confusing a low probability (a rare occurrence) with a high probability? A mailman thought, "They'll probably fire me for missing 3 days of work." But after he reflected on it, he asked himself, "When was the last time they fired anyone at the post office?"

11. Am I assuming every situation is the same? Are you taking into consideration time, location, and subtle differences? "Just because I dropped out of school 20 years ago doesn't mean I'll fail this time."

12. Am I focusing on irrelevant factors? Patients attempting to build a case for their depression have asked me, "What about Uganda, starving children, and Hitler?" It's highly unfortunate that there is misery and evil in the world. But it's irrelevant to being depressed. Do what you can to alleviate the suffering of others, but getting depressed over it won't help.

13. Am I overlooking my strengths? When people become depressed, they overlook the problems they have solved in the past. I am continually amazed at people's ability to handle adversity once they turn their thinking around. Ask yourself how you handled situations like these in the past.

14. What do I want? What are my goals? Do I want to be happy and get the most out of life? Is this thinking ("Everything's bad") getting me what I want? Is it doing me any good?

15. How would I look at this if I weren't depressed? Would I think a cold sore is the worst thing that could happen? How would others (nonpartisan viewers) interpret this situation? Imagine how you will react to it once you are over your depression.

16. What can I do to solve the problem? Are my thoughts leading to problem solving (generating solutions) or to problem blockage? If your kids are fighting and the plumbing is stopped up, thinking about the "unfairness of it all" doesn't lead to any solutions.

17. Am I asking myself questions that have no answers? ("How can I redo the past?" "How can I be someone different?" "How can a relationship that's ended not be over?") Questions like these often can only be answered with questions. "Why should this happen to me?" Answer: "Why shouldn't it?" "What if something terrible happens?" Answer: "So what if it does?" Asking yourself unanswerable questions is another way of demanding that the world be different than it is.

18. What are the distortions in my thinking? Once you pinpoint the errors, you can correct them. Are you jumping to conclusions? Painting everything black? Are you confusing your behavior with your worth?

19. What are the advantages and disadvantages of thinking this way? Ask if there are advantages in thinking, "I hate this house, I hate this neighborhood, and I hate this city and everything in it." Probably few. The disadvantage is that this type of thinking can stop you from getting your share of pleasure.

20. What difference will this make in a week, a year, or 10 years? Will anyone remember (let alone care) in 10 years that I made a stupid remark at a party or had dandruff on my sweater? People often believe that their mistakes will be frozen forever in others' minds.

5. *Action.* Just answering your thoughts won't be enough to get you over your depression. *You must act on your new thoughts and beliefs.* By acting differently, you can change old thinking habits and strengthen the new ones. You have to *do something* to challenge your automatic thoughts. Listed below are a number of approaches that have been effective for many people in changing their behavior and overcoming depression.

a. *Problem solving.* As individuals' drinking problems become more severe, a number of problems often develop in other areas of their lives. These may be in relationships with spouse, significant other, or family members; loss of job or a lack of vocational direction; financial difficulties; legal problems. Many times, the person feels overwhelmed by these problems, worries about them, begins to feel helpless over their outcomes, and starts to feel depressed.

NOTE: The following information is provided only as a review of general problem-solving strategies and may not be necessary to go over in detail, if at all, depending on the client's level of demonstrated skill in this area from previous sessions.

One way to try to deal with this form of depression is to use the general *problem-solving strategies* outlined in a previous session:

1. *Recognize the problem.* Does a problem exist? What are some of the clues that one does exist?

2. *Identify the problem.* What is the problem? Define it as specifically and concretely as possible, including its smaller parts.

3. *Consider various approaches.* What can I do to possibly solve this problem? Try brainstorming, changing your point of view or frame of reference, or adapting a solution that has worked before as ways to generate alternative solutions.

4. *Select the most promising approach.* The solution that maximizes positive outcomes and minimizes negative ones is the one to implement first.

5. *Assess the effectiveness of the selected approach.* How well did it work? Do I need to try a different approach?

Using a systematic problem-solving approach lets people feel that they have an impact on and control over problems in their lives. As the problems are put in a different perspective and hopefully solved, depression begins to fade and they begin to feel better about themselves.

b. *Change your activity level.* One of the ways shown to improve mood and depression is to increase involvement in positive activities and reduce involvement in negative ones. (A more detailed focus of increasing positive activities is found in another session of this manual.)

Why focus on increasing positive activities? First, *increasing your activity is a major way to change your thinking.* When you are depressed, you do less, blame yourself for doing less, and become more depressed and apathetic; doing more challenges these stances. Second, studies show that even very depressed persons feel better when they become more active; *activity improves mood*. Third, *activity counteracts the fatigue found in depression*; you have to do more to get more energy. Fourth, *activity increases one's motivation*; you have to do what you don't feel like doing before you feel like doing it. Fifth, *activity improves your mental ability*; you not only change your situation by action, but you stimulate yourself to think. Solutions to what seem like unsolvable problems come to mind as you begin moving. Sixth, *once you become more active, people will get off your back*. Usually others will respond positively to your attempts to become more active, providing a secondary source of reinforcement for continued change.

NOTE: The following information is provided only as a review of strategies involved in increasing pleasant activities and may not be necessary to go over in detail, if at all, depending on the client's level of demonstrated skill in this area from previous sessions.

Increasing Pleasant Activities: Positive Steps. People who are depressed often do not want to be involved in any activities and instead are inert. Developing a schedule of daily activities and following through with them is one way to help overcome depression. A number of steps have been found to help depressed individuals get going again:

a. *Develop a schedule* of activities that is *flexible* and allows for alternatives or contingencies if the activities you planned cannot be accomplished.

b. *Stick with the general plan.* If for some reason you cannot do the activity that you had planned, don't try to go back and make it up; just go on with the schedule.

c. *Schedule activities in one hour and half hour intervals.* Do not plan activities that are too specific or too general.

d. *Plan for quantity, not quality.* When you are depressed, anything worth doing is even worth doing poorly!

e. *Be task oriented.* Remember that your primary goal is to follow the schedule you have established for yourself. The focus is on becoming more active; lessening of depression will follow.

f. *After completing a planned day of activities, write down how you have done.* Look at what you did right and where you can improve. Again, do not expect to follow the schedule perfectly.

Increasing Positive Activities: Blocks to Action. Despite good intentions, depressed people are often able to come up with a number of reasons (rationalizations?) that keep them from engaging in positive activities:

a. *"I can't think of any activities to schedule."* Is it that you *cannot* or just that you are having trouble? In general, you can schedule three types of activities: (1) things that you must do daily (eat, dress); (2) things that bring you pleasure (going to a movie, reading, shopping), and (3) things that bring a sense of satisfaction or mastery (answering letters, finishing projects).

b. *"Practical problems stop me from carrying out activities."* Life is a series of practical problems that are more difficult to solve when exaggerated by depression; solving them often sets the stage for getting better. Use the general problem-solving approach to overcome these problems.

c. *"I'm not a recordkeeper—I can't keep a schedule."* While this may be a hassle, recordkeeping is not impossible! The key is to write down your activities in some form.

d. *"I get distracted and sidetracked and don't follow through on my schedule."* If this is a problem, see it as a challenge you can beat. Get rid of distractions; don't lie down during the day if you're depressed; use aids to help follow through on the schedule; reward yourself for following your schedule; plan activities for specific times, and make sure you follow through on time; develop cues to switch into your activity; start your plan with a success experience.

e. *"I'm so overwhelmed with problems that I can't get started."* Believing your problems are too much for you is part of depression; don't be overwhelmed by this sense of being overwhelmed. The *sense* of being overwhelmed is nearly always worse than the *reality* of the situation.

g. *Pace yourself.* As you start to become more active, you may try to do too much, especially if you've been depressed for a while. The drawback to becoming overly ambitious is that it can backfire, especially if you run into difficulty; it is easy to become discouraged. So stick to your plan and increase your activities *gradually.*

Decreasing Unpleasant Activities. Another way to combat feelings of sadness and depression is to decrease unpleasant activities. The following are some methods you can use to decrease unpleasant activities:

a. *Avoid the situation.* Engaging in the opposite action often solves the problem. Many unpleasant activities can simply be avoided.

b. *Change the situation.* Do some "engineering" that modifies the situation to make it more manageable or less aversive.

c. *Plan.* Good planning can prevent many unpleasant activities.

d. *Say "no."* Learn to say "no" to things that you do not want to do. This is probably the best way to ward off an unpleasant event.

e. *Master the problem.* Move toward an unpleasant activity instead of avoiding it. Embrace the activity and see if you can master it.

f. *Limit the activity.* If you just do not like some activity, "build a fence" around it. Give yourself a specific amount of time to work on it and no more.

g. *Be careful of your thoughts.* If you're bothered by *thoughts* of certain activities, separate the reality from what you imagine.

h. *Use the three A's.* Become *aware* of thoughts and images that are making events more unpleasant, *answer* them, then *act* on the new ones.

In-Session Exercise

Have clients describe their depression or an event that seems to contribute to their depression. Have them focus on the three *A's* involved in overcoming depression. What cues are they *aware* of in mood, thought, and behavior. Explore with clients the automatic negative thoughts about self and the world that underlie the depression or are manifested in the situation. Have clients *answer* these thoughts. Have them ask questions of the thoughts or perceptions of self or situation that are outlined in the skill guidelines. Have clients outline the *actions* that they will use to help challenge their thoughts and behave in a more positive way. This may include active problem solving or modifying positive or negative behaviors.

Managing Negative Moods and Depression

Reminder Sheet

Use the *Three A's* to help overcome your depression

- Be AWARE of the symptoms of depression.
  - Be aware of your moods and the situations that influence them.
  - Be aware of your automatic negative thoughts.
- ANSWER these thoughts.
  - Ask questions, challenge the assumptions behind these thoughts.
  - Replace the negative thoughts with positive ones.
- ACT differently.
  - Use your problem-solving skills to deal with issues that give you worries and concerns.
  - Increase your positive activities.
  - Decrease your involvement in unpleasant activities.
  - Reward yourself for the positive steps you are making.

Practice Exercise

Use this worksheet to help you become more aware of the issues involved in your depression and the active steps you can take to change your moods.

1. What are the ways that I show my depression in my moods, attitudes, and actions? What are my symptoms? _____
   _____
   _____

2. What are the automatic negative thoughts that go along with my depression? What do I think about myself, my current situation, and my world in general? _____
   _____
   _____

3. What questions can I ask myself to challenge these automatic negative thoughts? _____
   _____

4. What steps am I going to take to act differently? What problem-solving strategies have I come up with to deal with my problems? What pleasant activities might I increase? What unpleasant activities might I avoid or minimize? _____
   _____
   _____

Elective Session: Enhancing Social Support Networks

This session was taken from pages 72–76 of the Monti et al. book, with the following modifications.

Rationale

Add to rationale item 1:

It is important for abstinent drinkers to work on building social support systems. Often, in the course of a drinking career, drinkers' social circles narrow to include only other people who drink and who therefore will not be of much support in efforts to quit. Also, many drinkers find it hard to ask for help from family and friends because they feel they've disappointed those who have offered support many times in the past. If so, this might be a good time to hold a couples or family session, to go over how the family member can help you cope with situations that may be difficult for you.

Skill Guidelines

Add the following after item 2e:

f. *Help with not drinking.* Asking your spouse to talk with you or participate in a distracting activity when you are craving; asking a friend or coworker not to offer you drinks or talk about drinking when you are around; asking a parent to handle your money or paychecks for a few months so you don't have a lot of money lying around; asking a roommate who drinks not to drink around you (have you considered that you might need to get a new roommate?).

In-Session Exercise

The following exercise is added:

Make a diagram of your circle of social support. Put yourself in the center, the people who are already important in your life closest to you, people who are currently neutral a little farther away, and people you have not seen for a while or who are negative even farther away. Write in their roles (family, coworker, friend) and what kind of support they do (or could) offer. Circle the people who will be of most help in your efforts to not drink. What kind of support or help could you (or do you) provide them?

NOTE: In practice, one of the more convenient methods for enhancing a drinker's social support network is through involvement in self-help groups. However, in Project MATCH, a self-help, 12-Step facilitation approach is being contrasted with this cognitive-behavioral approach, so it is not permissible for a therapist to suggest or strongly encourage involvement in AA. If the patient suggests AA as a way of enhancing social supports, the therapist should not say anything more compelling than "That sounds like a good idea." Let it go at that, and go on to help the patient develop some other, non-AA strategies for enhancing social supports.

Elective Session: Job-Seeking Skills

Rationale

The Job Club is a disciplined approach to assist clients in obtaining satisfying employment. This approach to job finding uses behavioral principles.

A major premise of the Job Club is that finding a job is a full-time job, and all job seekers need to treat the problem as such. It must be emphasized that it is as important as therapy. The key elements to job finding are—

- Development of a resume.

- Instructions on how to fill out a job application.

- Using relatives, friends, and the phone book to generate job leads.

- Telephone techniques to secure interviews.

- Rehearsal of the interview process.

- Information on appropriate employment.

Skill Guidelines

The Resume

Developing a positive resume is one of the first tasks. A resume should not leave large gaps between jobs, even if the client was not working due to drinking. These gaps can be handled by stating that the client was self-employed or rethinking his career goals during that period. The resume should be professionally typed and a good cover letter should be developed with counselor assistance. There are forms in the *Job Club Counselor's Manual* (Azrin and Besalel 1980) to help clients develop resumes.

The Job Application	Filling out a job application correctly needs to be taught to many clients. They should learn how to emphasize positive personal attributes along with good job skills. Counselors need to work with the patients to make sure they understand how to correctly answer difficult questions.
Generating Job Leads	Job finding needs to be done in a matter of fact yet supportive manner. Clients will often take the easy way out and not comply with this critical aspect unless they are given a structure (e.g., the "Job Leads Log") and are monitored.

After completing the resume and learning how to fill out a job application, the patient needs to generate possible job leads. One way is to ask family and friends if they know of any possible employment opportunities. Another is to ask former employers and coworkers. If this fails to generate sufficient leads, advise the client to use the yellow pages of the phone book. For instance, if the client is looking for employment as a salesperson in a lumber yard, look in the yellow pages under lumber yards.

To document leads, have the client use the "Job Leads Log" included at the end of this section. It has a place for date, name of company and address, phone number, and space to jot down details during and after the phone call. There is also a place on this form for call backs if necessary. A minimum of 10 job leads are generated before the patient begins to make any phone calls. This list is checked by the counselor to assure that all leads are appropriate.

Telephone Skills Training

The next step is to rehearse telephone skills to make sure the client can use the telephone in a positive way. The following is a suggested outline:

- Introduce yourself by giving your name and then asking for the person who does the hiring.

- If you get this person on the line, again introduce yourself and make a statement like "I heard that ABC Lumber company is a good place to work, and I would like to come down and discuss with you my qualifications as a lumber yard worker. When can I meet with you?"

- If you do not get the person that does the hiring, ask for his or her name so you have it when you call back.

Other scenarios will occur, and each one has to be discussed and rehearsed so mastery is achieved. Try to get the name of the person who does the hiring beforehand, if possible, so you can ask directly for that person. This may be possible if you get the name from a friend or former coworker.

Rehearsal of Interview Process

After job leads are generated and phone calls have secured interviews, train the client, using behavioral rehearsal, in the interviewing process. Reinforce the client at each step of the process. Once clients are ready for the interview, make sure they have proper transportation. Clients must also be prepared to be rejected for employment.

Goal Setting

Each day, the client must get 10 new leads, make appropriate telephone calls, write necessary letters, and attend interviews. Success comes from making enough calls to secure enough interviews so the chances of getting a job increase to 100 percent.

Job-Seeking Skills

Reminder Sheet

1. Finding a job is a full-time job in itself, and you need to treat it as such.

2. The key elements include:

   a. developing a resume,

   b. knowing how to fill out a job application,

   c. using relatives, friends, and the phone book to generate job leads,

   d. using telephone techniques to secure interviews,

   e. rehearsing the interview process, and

   f. deciding what is appropriate employment.

Exercises

After this session, job finding should become a daily routine until you are successful in getting a job. Here is a suggested schedule:

1. Each evening, develop 10 job leads either through friends or with the Yellow Pages.

2. Get up at the same time each morning and begin making phone contacts at 8:00 a.m. Continue with this through the morning until the first scheduled job interview appointment in the afternoon. If unsuccessful in getting a job interview for the afternoon, spend the afternoon either making followup calls to companies contacted before or develop additional leads rather than waiting until the evening.

3. If you have the time, try to practice answering possible job interview questions with a friend or family member before going to an interview.

4. Spend the afternoon attending the job interview you scheduled that morning.

Continue with this daily schedule until you are successful. Remember that sticking with it is often the most important thing you can do to get a job.

Job Leads Log

Date	Company	Person's name	Telephone number	Address	Result of call	Second call		Third call	
						Date	Result	Date	Result

Elective Session: Couples/Family Involvement I

This session is directed toward couples. Appropriate adjustments can be made for use with other family members or significant others.

Rationale

1. We have asked you to come as a couple. This is because, as you know, drinking affects other areas of your life, including marriage and the family. Spouses usually have some feelings and reactions to their partner's drinking. Sometimes spouses try over and over to help their partners stop. Sometimes they give up or get angry. Sometimes their well-intentioned attempts to help are resented or make things worse in the long run. (Ask clients if any of these observations rings a bell in their lives and how they feel about the above).

2. We have also found that, in many couples, when one person has a drinking problem, there are also marital problems. For one reason or another, couples no longer get the positive rewards out of marriage and each other that they used to. Usually *communication between partners is poor*, nonexistent, or filled with negative emotions such as anger, withdrawal, heavy silence, or getting needs met outside the relationship (e.g., going out alone).

3. Another common marital difficulty is that small problems begin to get one down. It becomes harder to make even easy decisions. Eventually, they pile up so that essential tasks do not get done (shopping, paying bills, cleaning house, filling the car with gas). Couples begin to lose their ability to *make decisions or solve problems*. (Ask client if any of the above is relevant.)

4. Our goals are to—

NOTE: Adapted from Abrams et al. 1979, developed with support of NIAAA grant AA–07070, Barbara McCrady, Principal Investigator. The rationale section is taken directly from Session 1, pages 3–4. The Skill Guidelines #1 and the first two paragraphs of #2 are directly from Session 4, pages 31–32. Used with permission.

    a. Help you work together to achieve sobriety of the drinking partner.

    b. Increase the positive rewards in your marriage.

    c. Learn how to solve problems when they come up.

    d. Develop good communication skills.

Skill Guidelines

1. *Stimulus Control.* One type of situation that spouses are often concerned about is having alcohol in the house. Many times, a wife will feel that the stocked liquor cabinet, or beer in the refrigerator, is just too much of a trigger for drinking. Some problem drinkers feel similarly, while others find that alcohol in the house does not make much difference. (Ask couple: have the two of you thought about this? Have you discussed it with each other at all?)

   Have the couple discuss this topic with each other for a few minutes, trying to come to a decision about how they will handle alcohol in the house. As the therapist, help them follow good listening and communication skills. Encourage both of them to express their own feelings about whether or not to keep alcohol in the house. You may have to get them to paraphrase what the other person is saying to assure that they understand each other. Work toward an initial agreement that they both can live with, and have them implement it during the week.

2. *Reinforcing Sobriety.* Besides the one plan already discussed, there are some other ways to view spouse involvement in sobriety. Explain to the spouse that sober behavior can be made more likely by looking at the short-term consequences of staying sober. If people are specifically complimented (rewarded) for staying sober, not just taken for granted, then these pleasant short-term consequences can help them stay sober in the future.

   Have the couple come up with some desirable verbal statements that the spouse and drinker would like to hear, contingent on sobriety. Elicit from them an agreement on three or four verbal rewards that they would like to implement. Suggest that these be implemented for homework, at least one verbal reward per day contingent on sobriety.

   In addition to rewarding sobriety, the couple should also make plans to reward each other for some of the favors they do. Too often, alcohol-involved marriages slip into a cycle of mutual criticism and recriminations. This can be reversed by having each spouse make an effort to praise the other daily for some satisfaction or favor provided. To paraphrase a slogan from Parent Effectiveness Training, they should "catch each other being good." Have the spouses role play appropriate ways of giving verbal praise.

3. *Problem Solving.* The process by which problems are dealt with in a close relationship is a very important aspect of that relationship. Problem-solving skills have already been presented to the identified patient in an earlier session. The steps of that process should be reviewed at this time: (1) recognize that there is a problem, (2) identify the problem, (3) consider various approaches, (4) select the most promising approach, and (5) assess the effectiveness of the selected approach. Discuss each step in some detail with the couple to verify their understanding.

In-Session Exercise

Have the couple identify a problem situation they are presently coping with, or one they can anticipate in the near future. Have them work through each of the first four steps of the problem-solving process together. The therapist may serve as a resource to answer questions, provide suggestions if they get stuck, or keep them on track, but otherwise should let the couple work it through by themselves as much as possible. For the fifth step of the process, the couple should specify acceptable outcomes as well as outcomes that would necessitate a reworking of their approach.

Introducing the Practice Exercise

The assignment has several elements. Go over each one with the couple to make sure they understand what is to be done and how their behavior is to be recorded. Suggest that they continue practicing each element of the assignment regularly until the next conjoint session.

Schedule the next couples session in several weeks.

Couples/Family Involvement I

Reminder Sheet

1. The nonusing spouse should provide at least one verbal reward (praise) each day to the recovering drinker for continuing to be sober.

2. Both partners should praise each other at least once daily for satisfactions given to each other.

3. As problems are encountered, they should be dealt with by both spouses together, using the five-step problem-solving process:

   a. Recognize that a problem exists.

   b. Identify the problem as accurately as you can.

   c. Consider various approaches to solving the problem.

   d. Select the most promising approach.

   e. Assess the effectiveness of the selected approach.

Practice Exercises

1. Implement the plan you came up with during the treatment session regarding alcohol in the home.

2. The nonusing spouse should reward abstinent behavior verbally at least once each day.

3. Use the problem-solving process together at least once every week. Write a brief summary of what you did and how it worked. Bring these summaries to the next couples session.

Elective Session: Couples/Family Involvement II

Review of Practice Exercises

Review the couple's progress on their plans regarding alcohol in the house, the praise given for sobriety, and their summaries of problem-solving efforts, as assigned at the previous couples session. Provide as much praise as possible for their efforts and accomplishments. Trouble-shoot problem areas or reasons for non-compliance.

Rationale [1]

1. There are any number of possible barriers to closeness or intimacy in relationships. Can you generate some examples? These might include distrust, anger, poor self-esteem, fear of failure, withdrawal/isolation, or sex role typing.

2. Effective communication within close/intimate relationships is important for several reasons. Among them are the following:

   a. It helps you and your partner to feel closer to each other.

   b. It promotes better understanding of each other's point of view and increases your ability to solve difficulties and conflicts.

   c. It decreases the likelihood that resentment and bad feelings over something will build up and affect other areas of your life (e.g., daily bickering over finances or the in-laws may lead to more pervasive negative feelings).

   d. Drinking and relapse are less likely to occur when you have an effective way to respond to difficulties in a relationship.

---

1 The rationale and skill guidelines are taken directly from selected sections of the Monti et al. session on "Close and Intimate Relationships," pages 68–70.

Skill Guidelines [2]

1. *Do not expect your partner to read your mind.* That is, don't expect him/her to know what you think, want, or feel without your expressing it.

2. *Do not let things build up.* Frequent contact with a person increases the chance that some of his/her behaviors may bother you. Since the cumulative negative impact of saying nothing about a repeated annoyance can be great, it is important to *give constructive criticism* at an early point.

   When giving constructive criticism, calmly state the criticism in terms of your own feelings, focusing on the impact that the situation has on you. Criticize specific behavior (e.g., "*I feel* angry *when you* leave dirty dishes all over the kitchen") not the person, and request a change in that behavior (e.g., "I'd appreciate it if you'd remember to rinse your dishes off and put them in the sink when you're done with them"). Finally, offer to compromise, so that both of you can come away from the discussion feeling that you have gained something (e.g., "I'll wash the dishes if you leave them rinsed and in the sink").

   No matter how adept you are at giving criticism appropriately, you must be selective. Stop and think before commenting on irritations. Do not bring them up unless they seem important to you. Bringing up every minor annoyance can put your partner permanently on the defensive.

3. *Express your positive feelings.* Many couples have difficulty expressing positive feelings within their relationship, particularly if the level of criticism has been increasing. When criticism occurs in the absence of any expression of positive affect, good feelings get overlooked, and negative feelings become more salient.

   One reason people become reluctant to express positive feelings is the fear that doing so would contradict the criticisms they have made. For example, one partner may refrain from saying that a dinner is good if he/she has criticized the other partner for serving it an hour later than expected. However, it is not inconsistent to verbalize both of these aspects of our reactions to another person's behavior. A problem arises when we assume that positive verbalizations are not important because "he knows how I feel even if I don't say it."

---

[2] The last two paragraphs of the skill guidelines (4 and 5) are taken directly from Abrams et al. 1979, page 58.

4. Couples may negotiate fun activities by using quid pro quos. ("I'll do what you want today in exchange for you doing what I want over the weekend.")

5. Go out of your way to offer to do necessary but irksome tasks around the house. Offer to do tasks that one's partner usually does or complains about. Give to the other without expecting anything back and without saying, I'll do it only if you do something for me.

Behavioral Rehearsal Role Plays

Ask the couple to identify some situations that are problematic for them. Select one for role playing now and one for the practice exercise. Have the couple discuss how the application of some of the communications skills discussed could help them cope more effectively with the situation selected for role playing. Then have the couple role play the situation, trying to employ those skills. The therapist should provide feedback regarding both the verbal and nonverbal aspects of the role play.

Wrap-Up

Ask the couple to summarize what was most salient and useful from these two couples sessions. What do they plan to practice/apply in the future?

Introducing the Practice Exercise

Although the couple will not have an opportunity to turn in the completed exercise, they should be urged to complete it as a way of continuing the practice they began in the role playing. They should also be urged to make an effort to apply these principles in their relationship on an ongoing basis.

Couples/Family Involvement II [3]

Reminder Sheet

The following points can be of assistance to you within a close relationship:

- Do not expect your partner to read your mind.

- Do not let things build up: Give constructive criticism.

- Calm down.

- Stop and think before expressing irritation.

- State the criticism in terms of your own feelings.

- Criticize specific behavior, not the person.

- Request specific behavior change.

- Offer to compromise.

- Express your positive feelings.

- Offer to go along with a fun activity in exchange for doing one that you choose at a later time.

- Offer to do necessary but irksome tasks around the house.

Practice Exercise

Use the practice exercise in Monti et al., pages 207–208.

---

3 The Reminder Sheet is adapted from Monti et al., page 207.

Appendix A—Bibliography

This manual represents a compilation of materials from a number of sources. Peter Monti, David Abrams, Ronald Kadden and Ned Cooney's *Treating Alcohol Dependence: A Coping Skills Training Guide*, © Guilford Press, 1989, served as the primary source for the Project MATCH CBT therapists' manual and the introduction of this volume. Other sources are listed by chapter.

Introduction to Coping Skills Training

Litt, M. "Introduction to Coping Skills Training." Unpublished manuscript, University of Connecticut Health Center, Farmington, CT, 1990.

Jaffe, A.; Brown, J.; Korner, P.; and Witte, G. "Relapse Prevention for the Treatment of Problem Drinking: A Manual for Therapists and Patients." Unpublished manuscript, Yale University School of Medicine, New Haven, CT; University of Connecticut Health Center, Farmington, CT, 1988.

Coping with Cravings and Urges to Drink

Carroll, K. "Manual for Relapse Prevention in the Treatment of Cocaine Abuse." Unpublished manuscript, Yale University School of Medicine, New Haven, CT, 1987.

Ito, J.R.; McNair, L.; Donovan, D.M.; and Marlatt, G.A. "Relapse Prevention for Alcoholism Aftercare: Treatment Manual." Unpublished manuscript, Health Services Research and Development Service, VA Medical Center, Seattle, WA, 1984.

Jaffe, A.; Brown, J.; Korner, P.; and Witte, G. "Relapse Prevention for the Treatment of Problem Drinking: A Manual for Therapists and Patients." Unpublished manuscript, Yale University School of Medicine, New Haven, CT; University of Connecticut Health Center, Farmington, CT, 1988.

Managing Thoughts About Alcohol and Drinking

Ito, J.R.; McNair, L.; Donovan, D.M.; and Marlatt, G.A. "Relapse Prevention for Alcoholism Aftercare: Treatment Manual."

Unpublished manuscript, Health Services Research and Development Service, VA Medical Center, Seattle, Washington, 1984.

Ludwig, A.M. *Understanding the Alcoholic's Mind: The Nature of Craving and How to Control It.* New York: Oxford University Press, 1988.

Problem Solving

Bedell, J.R.; Archer, R.P.; and Marlowe, H.A. A description and evaluation of a problem solving skills training program. In: Upper, D., and Ross, S.M., eds. *Behavioral Group Therapy: An Annual Review.* Champaign, IL: Research Press, 1980.

D'Zurilla, T.J., and Goldfried, M.R. Problem solving and behavior modification. *Journal of Abnormal Psychology* 78:107–126, 1971.

Sanchez-Craig, M. "A Therapist's Manual for Secondary Prevention of Alcohol Problems." Unpublished manual. Addiction Research Foundation, Toronto, Canada, 1983.

Planning for Emergencies and Coping with a Lapse

Jaffe, A.; Brown, J.; Korner, P.; and Witte, G. "Relapse Prevention for the Treatment of Problem Drinking: A Manual for Therapists and Patients." Unpublished manuscript, Yale University School of Medicine, New Haven, CT; University of Connecticut Health Center, Farmington, CT, 1988.

Seemingly Irrelevant Decisions

Marlatt, G.A., and Gordon, J.R. *Relapse Prevention: Maintenance Strategies in the Treatment of Addictive Behaviors.* New York: Guilford Press, 1985.

Managing Negative Moods and Depression

Emery, G. *A New Beginning: How to Change Your Life Through Cognitive Therapy.* New York: Simon and Schuster, 1981.

Enhancing Social Support Networks

Depue, J. Getting a little help from your friends. In: Depue, J. ed. *Managing Stress* (Pawtucket Heart Health Program treatment manual). Pawtucket, RI: The Memorial Hospital, 1982. pp. 1–9.

Marlatt, G.A., and Gordon, J.R. *Relapse Prevention: Maintenance Strategies in the Treatment of Addictive Behaviors.* New York: Guilford Press, 1985.

Job Seeking Skills

Azrin, N.H., and Besalel, V.A. *Job Club Counselor's Manual.* Baltimore, MD: University Park Press, 1980.

Meyers, R.J.; Smith, J.E.; and Mallams, J.H. "The Community Reinforcement Approach Manual." Unpublished manuscript, University of New Mexico, Albuquerque, NM, 1992.

Couples/Family Involvement

Abrams, D.B.; McCrady, B.S.; and Hay, W. "Treatment Manual: Self-Control Treatment With Spouse Involved and Marital Therapy." Unpublished manual, Butler Hospital/Brown University, 1979.

General Background Materials

Annis, H.M., and Davis, C.S. Relapse prevention. In: Hester, R.K., and Miller, W.R., eds. *Handbook of Alcoholism Treatment Approaches.* New York: Pergamon, 1989. pp. 170–182.

Chaney, E.F. Social skills training. In: Hester, R.K., and Miller, W.R., eds. *Handbook of Alcoholism Treatment Approaches.* New York: Pergamon, 1989. pp. 206–221.

Daley, D.C. *Relapse: A Guide to Successful Recovery.* Bradenton, FL: Human Services Institute, 1987.

Donovan, D.M., and Chaney, E.F. Alcoholic relapse prevention and intervention: Models and methods. In: Marlatt, G.A., and Gordon, J.R., eds. *Relapse Prevention: Maintenance Strategies in the Treatment of Addictive Behaviors.* New York: Guilford Press, 1985. pp. 351–416.

Ito, J.R., and Donovan, D.M. Aftercare in alcoholism treatment: A review. In: Miller, W.R., and Heather, N., eds. *Treating Addictive Behaviors: Processes of Change.* New York: Plenum, 1986. pp. 435–456.

Ito, J.R.; Donovan, D.M.; and Hall, J.J. Relapse prevention in alcohol aftercare: Effects on drinking outcome, change process, and aftercare attendance. *British Journal of Addiction* 83:171–181, 1988.

Kadden, R.M.; Cooney, N.L.; Getter, H.; and Litt, M.D. Matching alcoholics to coping skills or interactional therapies: Posttreatment results. *Journal of Consulting and Clinical Psychology* 57:698–704, 1989.

Marlatt, G.A., and Gordon, J.R. *Relapse Prevention: Maintenance Strategies in the Treatment of Addictive Behaviors.* New York: Guilford Press, 1985.

Appendix B: Therapist Selection, Training, and Supervision in Project MATCH

Specifications of treatment in manuals is intended to define and differentiate psychotherapies, to standardize therapist technique, and to permit replication by other investigators. However, it is essential that manual-guided therapies be implemented by qualified therapists who are trained to perform them effectively. Project MATCH uses extensive procedures to select, train, and monitor therapists in order to promote delivery of study treatments that are specific, discriminable, and delivered at a consistently high level of quality. These include (1) selection of experienced therapists committed to the type of therapy they would be performing, (2) extensive training to help therapists modify their repertoire to meet manual guidelines and to standardize performance across therapists and across sites, and (3) ongoing monitoring and supervision of each therapist's delivery of treatment during the main phase of the study to assure implementation of study treatments at a high and consistent level.

Therapist Selection

All MATCH therapist candidates are required to meet the following selection criteria: (1) completion of a master's degree or above in counseling, psychology, social work, or a closely related field (some exceptions to this requirement were made in individual cases), (2) at least 2 years of clinical experience after completion of degree or certification, (3) appropriate therapist technique, based on a videotaped example of a therapy session with an actual client submitted to the principal investigator at each site and to the Yale Coordinating Center, and (4) experience in conducting a type of treatment consistent with the MATCH treatment they would be conducting and experience treating alcoholics or a closely related clinical population.

These criteria are intended to facilitate (1) selection of appropriate therapists for the training program, as training is *not* intended to train novice therapists, but to familiarize experienced therapists with manual-guided therapy, and (2) implementation of MATCH treatments by experienced and credible therapists. For example, therapists selected for the Cognitive-Behavioral Coping Skills Therapy (CB) are experienced in cognitive and behavioral techniques; thus, the CB therapists are predominantly doctoral or masters-level psychologists. Therapists for the Twelve-Step Facilitation Program are predominantly individuals who have gone through 12-step recovery themselves, have been abstinent for several years, and are typically masters-level or certified alcoholism counselors. Therapists selected for the recently developed Motivation Enhancement Therapy (MET) have worked extensively with alcoholics and typically have experience in systems theory, family therapy, and motivational counseling.

Therapist Training

Training, supervision, and certification of therapists was centralized at the Yale Coordinating Center to facilitate consistency of treatment delivery across sites. Each therapist came to New Haven for a 3-day intensive training seminar, which included background and rationale for Project MATCH, extensive review of the treatment manual, review of taped examples of MATCH sessions, and practice exercises. Each therapist then returned to their clinical site and was assigned a minimum of two training cases, which were conducted following the MATCH protocol (e.g., weekly individual sessions, a maximum of two emergency and two conjoint sessions, truncated sessions for patients who arrived for a treatment session intoxicated).

All sessions from training cases were videotaped and sent to the Coordinating Center for review of the therapists' (1) adherence to manual guidelines, (2) level of skillfulness in treatment delivery, (3) appropriate structure and focus, (4) empathy and facilitation of the therapeutic alliance, and (5) nonverbal behavior. Yale Coordinating Center supervisors review all training sessions and provide weekly individual supervision to each therapist via telephone. Supplemental onsite supervision is delivered weekly by the project coordinator at each Clinical Research Unit.

Therapists were certified by the Yale Coordinating Center supervisors following successful completion of training cases. Therapists whose performance on initial cases was inadequate were assigned additional training cases until their performance improved. The average number of training cases was three, and therapists completed an average of 26 supervised sessions before certification.

Ongoing Monitoring

To monitor implementation of Project MATCH treatments, facilitate consistency of treatment quality and delivery across sites, and prevent therapist "drift" during the main phase of the study, all sessions are videotaped and sent to the Coordinating Center, where a proportion of each subject's sessions (one-third of all sessions for Cognitive-

Behavioral and Twelve-Step Facilitation, one half of all MET sessions) are reviewed by the supervisors. Telephone supervision is provided on a monthly basis by the Coordinating Center supervisors and supplemented with weekly onsite group supervision at each Clinical Research Unit.

All sessions viewed are rated for therapist skillfulness, adherence to manual guidelines, and delivery of manual-specified active ingredients unique to each approach. These ratings are sent monthly to the project coordinators at each site to alert local supervisors to therapist drift. Therapists whose performance deviates in quality or adherence to the manual are "redlined" by the Coordinating Center, and the frequency of sessions monitored and supervision is increased until the therapist's performance returns to acceptable levels.